THIS IS A NEEDED BOOK FOR THIS HOUR!

In How to Laugh Yourself Well - Body, Soul, and Spirit, Kristina teaches us that supernatural joy is possible, and that God loves when we laugh! "You will show me the path of life; in Your presence is fullness of joy; at Your right hand are pleasures forevermore" (Psalm 16:11). As someone passionate about pursuing joy and laughter, I can confidently say Kristina's book will bless you. She reveals to us that laughter is God's idea, and that joy is a powerful weapon to change the narrative of our lives. I appreciate and admire Kristina's journey of embracing joy for herself and how she inspires others to do the same. As you read this book, I believe you will get a radical breakthrough through the revelation and practical keys in it. Well done, Kristina!

Steve Backlund
Founder of Igniting Hope Ministries

HOW TO LAUGH YOURSELF WELL - BODY, SOUL & SPIRIT

It's Just a Laughing Matter

Kristina Khan

Leadership Consultant & Trainer Creator of
"Hilarious Love" Online Course

Dedication

I would like to first dedicate this book to the Lord and love of my life, Jesus Christ. Thank you, Father God, for showing me this gift and Holy Spirit for teaching me how to grow in laughter each day. Also, for sending a perfect stranger to confirm for me to write the book.

Next, I want to dedicate this book to my two beautiful children, whom I love more than life, Courtni and Wyatt for asking me why I was so happy after my trip to Africa which caused me to go on a journey to learn how to stay joyful.

Also, to my selfless mom Charlene for endless days and nights of transcribing and keeping the course when I wanted to quit, and for my wonderful and amazing husband, Ethan who has been my biggest fan and cheerleader in this process. I love you, Ethan!

I also want to thank Steve, Brian, and Tom for believing in and encouraging me. I am humbled and honored. Lastly, to all my family and friends as well as Stephanie, Alexis, Becky, Rebecca, and Lisa – thank you for all your support and encouragement.

I love and bless each one of you! ~ Kristina

CONTENTS

Forward

Over the years, Kristina has been used by God to train and equip the Body of Christ on so many levels. I have witnessed how she successfully helped lead many into a supernatural overcoming lifestyle.

But when Kristina discovered the power of utilizing joy as a weapon in the Heavenly realm it took the power of healing and deliverance to new levels. I saw how Kristina was able to lead others to even greater places of victory in the face of spiritual opposition. What a powerful tool.

I'm very glad Kristina put her lessons in a book, so I can read and reread these valuable keys while strengthening my own walk with God. As you can imagine, whenever you are in a trial it is going to be helpful to have this information right at your fingertips. As a Pastor, I am looking forward to sharing these books with members of our congregation so they can gain victory in their battles.

Thank you for all the love and dedication it took to put this book together, Kristina.

-Pastor Tom Schermitzler, God's Living Room

My sister's life journey thus far has been for the benefit of others. Her pursuit of helping everyone else sees no boundaries. She has circled the globe spreading a powerful weapon infused in her DNA, smile and laughter. I am excited to see Kristina do something for herself. This book's transparent insight is without limitations and has been therapeutic for her. Be prepared to experience an emotional roller coaster that will pilot you back to her purpose. Smiling and laughing through and with your circumstances. Hopefully, my sister's personal life experiences will comfort you wherever you are. Hold firmly to the belief that God's supernatural weapon is installed in all of us just as my sister has.

-Brian McKee

Introduction

I want to begin this book by sharing my testimony with you. Growing up I was given the nickname "Kristina, Kristina, the laughing hyena." I was young when I was called this. Maybe for you, being called that wouldn't have been such a big deal. But for me, it was the worst name anyone could call me. They were likely attempting to annoy me with what they considered a silly rhyme and it worked. However, they didn't call me that because I was always laughing. Instead, it was quite the opposite.

As a child, I remember being told to stop frowning. I didn't realize I was frowning all the time. I kept trying to change this behavior. But the more I tried to change it the more I seemed to do it. At the time, I didn't realize how often I frowned. I wasn't intentionally trying to frown or have a grimace on my face. Perhaps I wouldn't have such a pronounced frown line on my forehead today if I had listened.

But I absolutely hated the nickname I had been given, and unfortunately, it stuck. It became my identity for a long time. Let me ask you a question, have you ever seen a laughing hyena? If you have, you know they are not the cutest animal in the world. They are some of the ugliest animals and I did not want my name associated with that creature.

I didn't know the impact that childish rhyme would have on me later in life. For me, this jargon became my identity. I thought I was ugly, and that my name was ugly because of how ugly the animal was. I didn't think much of myself because of what I was identifying with this animal. People weren't trying to hurt me on purpose, but it stuck for a long time.

When people carry inner wounds, they tend to have low self-esteem. That was me. I was sensitive to the name. The words of that horrible nickname stuck to me like superglue. If you've ever tried to separate something joined together by superglue, you usually rip both things apart when you try to split them. My negative identity as a young child felt superglued to me and I was shaped in a very negative fashion because of it. It affected me so negatively that I wanted to change my name.

I knew I couldn't legally change my name as a little girl. But I wanted to ensure that no one I knew or met would ever call me Kristina. As a result of that little rhyme, I decided to replace Kristina with Kris and Kristi, because they were my favorite nicknames. I thought if people called me Kristi or Kris, then no one would know that I had changed my name. Fortunately, most of my family members called me Kristi or Kris. I honestly thought if I changed my name, it might change my identity. But that wasn't true. The damage from that nickname had already been done.

I didn't realize that a lie from the enemy had been planted so deep within me. The enemy was telling me, *"You are ugly and unimportant."* This lie caused me years of undiagnosed depression and struggles with weight issues. No matter how much I wanted to be seen as beautiful, the lie of the enemy kept me from knowing my true value and beauty. My self-esteem was negatively affected by the endless teasing. Having this name hanging over me, my childhood was not the happiest. My parents divorced when I was eight years old. Until my mother remarried when I was ten, my brothers and I were raised in a single-parent home.

My new stepfather treated me like a princess, and it was as if my days of low self-esteem were gone for good. But I had no idea he was grooming me for a more sinister plan. After my stepfather gained my trust and affection, the relationship changed. I thought he loved me, but I soon realized that wasn't the case. The so-called "love" he showed me came at a very high price for me, both emotionally and mentally. My stepfather began sexually abusing me for over a year. My innocence was being robbed each day, minute by minute. I felt trapped and depressed.

I got another rude awakening when I said I'd tell someone. My stepfather showed me a gun and said he'd use it on me or my family if I ever told anyone. These threats further pushed me into more profound pain and even deeper depression. Even though I felt like I was falling apart, I tried to look okay on the outside. I wore my mask daily. I planned to move out of my house without anyone knowing what was happening behind the scenes.

I took advantage of the fact that my stepfather had started drinking to get myself out of the house. I moved out at thirteen years old and began staying with friends from week to week. Finally, one of my friends' parents offered me the opportunity to live with them permanently. I lived there for about a year before moving in with my aunt and uncle.

I am sharing my story to illustrate that I wasn't raised in a loving and happy environment. My upbringing affected who I was and how I viewed myself. I felt hopeless and depressed. Because I was afraid of being hurt, I kept all my misery hidden from my family. Every aspect of my life was affected by this hidden pain.

Ultimately, the truth about my stepfather came out which was not well received by the people around me. Some family members couldn't believe what I had been through, which further contributed to my depression. He eventually was sentenced and went to prison. After that, I attempted to hide it, but it always came out in different ways, from self-esteem issues to being a people pleaser to everyone.

Eventually, I sought therapy and after a couple of years felt that I had overcome my past. I graduated from high school, went to a trade school, and got married at twenty years old. Little did I know that the depression I had pushed deep down was still inside me, it never left but stayed hidden. Did you know that you can be depressed and not be aware of it? Over the years, I became very good at covering my pain with a smile.

I had been raised in church my whole life, but I didn't have a relationship with Jesus. I talked about Him and could discuss spiritual things with others, but I eventually realized all I had was religion. My husband didn't have faith and had never gone to church. When we married, I expressed to him that I wanted to experience Christ with him.

I was raised in a family where the girls went to church, and the men stayed home and watched sports, and I wanted things to be different for us. He agreed to go with me. However, even though someone goes to church with you, you can't force them to change. And I needed to change too. Religion without relationship never works. Throughout our marriage, we had many struggles which caused neither of us to really feel valued or loved. I fooled myself into thinking that by changing my name and being married, I would be able to fill the voids in my life. Instead, I learned that changing my name didn't undo the damage caused by my past.

I then hit a low point I had never experienced before. After fourteen years of marriage, my husband left me for another woman. I was so down and so depressed that I considered suicide several times in hopes that it would make the sadness disappear. On the day I wanted to end it all, I cried out to God and said, "If only I could touch the hem of your garment, Jesus! I would be made whole."

By God's mercy and grace, I am still here to share that God took a horrible situation and turned it around for good. He touched my life and suddenly in that moment, I had a reason to continue to live. If not for myself, then for my two children. Perhaps you are wondering what all of this has to do with laughter. Keep reading.

When I thought of ending it all during my lowest point, I reached out for help. I cried out to Jesus. When I cried out to Jesus, He answered me in such a tangible way that it changed the course of my life. I still felt pain, but for the first time, I felt hope.

My whole life, I had attended church and Sunday school, but I had never had a real encounter with Jesus. I sang about Him and memorized many scriptures, but I did not know Jesus as my personal Savior. I had religion but no real relationship with God.

But something had changed, and I began to feel different. I began to feel peace. However, it would take some time to unravel the pain I had locked and hidden inside me as a child. After pursuing God for more than two years, I decided it was time to share the peace I had found in Jesus with others.

I began serving at several local churches, and soon I was helping to facilitate a weekly ministry that met at a little coffee house. During this time, the Lord spoke to me and said, *"I am going to change your name."* I replied, "Praise God! I get a new name; I'm so excited!"

After the coffee house ministry one night, I drove a lady home. She said, "Goodbye, Kristina," and opened the car door.

It seemed like something pierced my heart, and I knew there was something different right then. However, I refused to embrace my new identity as Kristina.

"What?" I asked. "No!" You don't understand. I ran from that name. I don't want to be known as Kristina.

Nothing changed. My name remained the same until I moved to California. After that, I started using my real name, Kristina. Having never lived in this city or state before, no one knew me, and this was a great place to start over. Then, one night I had a dream, and the Lord showed me my name and what it meant. You see the Lord knows everything about us and cares about everything that we carry in our souls.

I had previously seen books and knick-knacks personalized with my name. They said things like "little Christian" and "follower of Christ." I didn't know the value of my name until the Lord broke it down and showed it to me. My name means: "Christ in ya,"- "Christ in you, the hope of glory" taken from Colossians 1:27 in the Bible.

I suddenly realized that I wasn't just a follower of Christ, as it said on those little trinkets. In a flash, I understood; my name had great value and I wanted to use it all the time. Since Jesus had shown me that my name was valuable, I felt I had something to offer others - the man Christ. After so many years, the laughing hyena saga seemed like a distant memory. Now, I could call myself Kristina again.

A few years passed and unfortunately, the laughing hyena title resurfaced again. A friend received a prophetic word about being a laughing hyena and shared it with me. To my utter shock, they said to me, "Hey, Kristina, I feel like you are a laughing hyena too." I instantly felt dread come over me.

I was shocked that someone had once again called me a laughing hyena. It seemed like a terrible joke, and I was mortified. Then, I listened to the prophetic word a friend gave me that explained why the people felt I was a laughing hyena despite my feelings. For the first time in my life, I embraced the title "laughing hyena" and my name because I now understood I was to bring joy everywhere.

My spirit resonated with the prophetic word concerning the hyena. I told my friend how I had run from my name since I was a child because I didn't want to be called "Kristina, Kristina, the laughing hyena." However, after hearing the prophetic word I knew I wanted to be like a laughing hyena for the rest of my life. Through God's mercy and grace, the nickname that once brought me pain and suffering finally brought me closer to God, allowing me to see redemption in a place I didn't ever expect to find any. I learned the beauty of my name and embraced it wholeheartedly.

Just as I discovered, every one of you reading this has something to give. You have Christ in you, and it is the hope of glory! Let that sink into your spirit.

It was just the beginning of the journey God planned for me. Not one filled with pain or hurt, but one filled with laughter and God's eternal joy. As you read my story and others' testimonies in the following pages, I pray that you will experience a transformation within your own life. When we are full of joy, something changes. Having joy will become your new normal. God's joy will be your portion.

I believe that if you woke up this morning, God has a great plan for you. God has a purpose for you, and He can do something incredible with your life if you let Him.

CHAPTER ONE

Pure Joy

One year before I received the prophetic word about being a laughing hyena, I had the opportunity to go on a mission trip to South Africa. That was a shock, as I had really wanted to go to another country. I had said, "Lord, you can send me anywhere, just not Africa."

Now before you get upset, let me explain. I had grown up watching commercials on tv about the starvation of children in Africa, and every time I saw them, I wanted to cry. To see the children's bellies swollen and malnourished broke my heart. I didn't think I would ever be able to go to such a place without crying all the time.

Well, God had a different plan for my life which included Africa of all places and I am so thankful He did. When I found out I was going, I was excited and nervous due to my preconceived perception of Africa.

Let me begin by expressing how much I love South Africa. It was there that God changed my life. Even today, I would return to Africa in a heartbeat. That is where my testimony of how I received joy from the Lord happened. As you read, please take it in for yourself because the testimony of Jesus is the Spirit of prophecy.

I became aware of a gift that I had unknowingly carried during this trip. I also received understanding in a much deeper way that allowed me to be free from depression and anxiety for the first time. Do you want to know what this gift is? It's called laughter. God had to send me across the world to find it. Lucky for you, all you need to do is read this book.

In South Africa, I traveled with a ministry team, and we stayed at a resort called Pure Joy. Yes, it's true. I was at Pure Joy with twenty-four on fire, radical Jesus lovers. Talk about a set-up from God.

Every day, we went into the community, where we loved and ministered to many different people. Despite being one of the oldest team members, this was a new experience. I had never been part of anything like this before in my life. We ministered in orphanages and hospitals, to women selling themselves on the streets, spent time with AIDS babies, and even ministered to men in a local prison one day, to name a few.

We even witnessed someone lying in the middle of the street who was hit by a car. His name was Injustice. He died right there in front of us. Because the Lord calls us to heal the sick, raise the dead, and cast out demons in the Bible, we asked the bus driver to stop the bus so we could go pray for him.

We believed that this man would be raised from the dead. We prayed for over forty-five minutes. However, he never woke up. But we had the opportunity to pray for his friends and family, who were there weeping as we came near. We thought we were going for one reason, but God wanted us to go for another. He wanted us to minister to the man's friends and family that were so broken-hearted. When we got back on the bus, it was quieter than usual. Everyone was trying to process what had just happened. It's not every day that you pull over and can pray for the dead.

I was feeling a little overwhelmed with all the new experiences we encountered on our trip, and it was only the second day. I knew then that this would be a ministry trip I would never forget. I realized then how vital it would be for me to get up and spend time with God every day so I could minister without feeling discouraged.

Everywhere we went, we shared the Gospel and ministered to people in jam-packed crowds. Since I was responsible for waking everyone up in the morning, I would wake up extra early to have alone time to pray with

God before our day started. Early one morning my life was dramatically altered by a supernatural encounter.

I was standing in the yard, on what seemed a regular day. I was listening to worship music on my MP3 player, when it just stopped working. I considered going inside and getting another battery, but that would have interrupted my time with Jesus. So, I just started singing all of the Scripture songs I knew.

Even though I had run out of songs to sing, I still had some time left, so I opened my Bible. I began singing Psalms, and something started happening.

Psalm 16:11 *NJKV* says, *"...in Your presence is fullness of joy."* So, my first thought was, I'll just stay here for a little longer and linger with the Holy Spirit in His presence.

First, I began to sing the Psalms I knew, like Psalm 5:1 *NKJV*, which says, *"Give ear to my words, O Lord, consider my meditation."* After singing the entire scripture passage, I began to sing another passage *"As the deer pants for the water, so my soul longeth after thee,"* taken from Psalm 41. This verse in the book of Psalms summed up precisely what I was feeling at the time. My soul longed for the Lord. I wanted to spend time with my Heavenly Father, my Daddy.

As I sat in God's presence, something began to happen. Joy began to rise within me. I started chuckling deep inside as I continued to sing. I sang out Psalm 19:1-2 *NKJV*, *"The heavens declare the glory of God; and the firmament shows his handiwork. Day unto day utters speech, and night unto night reveals knowledge."*

I randomly selected verses from each chapter and came up with my own unique melody. The more I sang, the more I began to laugh. Pretty soon I couldn't stop laughing. But I didn't want to stop. I was experiencing a new form of joy I had never experienced before. It was wonderful.

Before I knew it, I was rolling on the grass and laughing hysterically. There was nobody tickling me or telling me a funny story. I was only singing the Psalms and laughing from a place deep down inside. God blessed me with unspeakable joy in the place called Pure Joy.

Before I knew it, time had sped away. I was supposed to be waking up the rest of the mission team. However, this morning would not be a typical wake-up call for the other members of our ministry team due to my encounter with the Lord. Instead, it would be a vastly different morning because I was experiencing joy like never before.

This morning marked the beginning of an all-day encounter with the Lord that was not quiet. He met me with joy and laughter in my quiet time. I carried this gift with me all along but had never experienced it.

Because I was one of the only members of our team who brought a battery alarm clock on the trip, my duty was to wake the team up so they could get ready to start their day. As I tried to walk back to the cabin, it felt like I had been drinking. I felt like I was literally drunk. It felt like I had consumed a bit of wine or champagne, and I suddenly felt off-kilter. I felt unbalanced, cracking up in laughter, and could not contain this deep well of emotional laughter. Cooks were standing outside and noticed my difficulty walking as I made my way to the cabins. I appeared intoxicated, stumbling, and bending over with big belly laughs.

The cooks at the resort prepared an elaborate spread of delicious food every morning—yep, we were suffering for Jesus.

As I staggered by, they appeared confused about why I was laughing. Several shouted, "Why are you so happy?" They began to laugh at the sight of my outburst of laughter.

Then they said, "It is too early to be this happy. You haven't even had coffee yet."

I replied, "Ha, ha, ha, I don't know, ha ha ha everything is just so funny." However, the coffee comment made me chuckle. At the time, I had not had any coffee in more than six years. So, I laughed even harder when I heard that remark from the cooks.

The closer I walked toward them, the louder they started to laugh. Remember that no funny joke was shared, and the cooks had no idea about my coffee story. They only knew that they could see a lady full of joy and laughter. I had no help from caffeine or anything else to initiate it.

They didn't realize that I had just encountered God's joy. I had the greatest gift of all, and it was contagious!

As I continued to walk back to my cabin and prepare for the day, my roommate saw me and called out for my help. She asked me to pray for a lady who was experiencing chest pain. At that moment, when I met them, I wasn't praying for anyone; I was laughing. So, my teammate took my hand and put it on the woman's chest. Instantly, the lady flew backward and landed on her back, but she stood up just as fast and shouted, "The pain! The pain! It is all gone!"

Somehow that made me laugh even more. I couldn't figure out what in the world was going on. I saw this lady fly back as if something had thrown her backward, but no one was near her.

Because I was laughing, and I could not stop, it was almost impossible for me to do anything else. A little while later, I was asked to lay hands and impart joy to everyone on our team. Again, my reaction was to laugh. The team was staring back at me with straight faces; as if to say, "Are you kidding me?" They hadn't had their coffee, and they were slightly annoyed because I was so full of joy.

I went to breakfast that morning and tried to eat, but my body would shake so much until all the food flew right off my fork and onto everyone else's plates. I tried to hold my mouth closed as well. But because of the laughter, all the food flew out also. I did everything under the sun, attempting to keep food in my mouth. Unfortunately, that wasn't the best way to make new friends.

Since I couldn't stop laughing and wasn't having much success eating breakfast, I irritated everyone. Talk about being a spectacle! I was one of the oldest people on the team and didn't want to make this kind of impression with food spraying out of my mouth because I was laughing and couldn't stop.

You might be thinking this is ridiculous. God would never do that. Well, guess what? He did, and I am telling you I could not stop it even though I tried.

People commented, "I think you are supposed to be fasting." But I wasn't. I was still trying to eat, but it was not working. Some would think this would be a sober moment and that I would get my act together, but guess what? I couldn't, and I just kept laughing.

Finally, after making everyone upset with me, I decided to go outside and sit by the pool. I laid down and began having a conversation with God. That is when God spoke to me about the call on my life.

I prayed, "Lord, you are doing something, but I don't know what You are doing. No one else understands what I'm experiencing, so I will spend time laughing with You because I don't know what else to do. I can't do anything else; it's like I can't stop."

Then I heard the Lord say, "Just like Jeremiah was called to be a weeping prophet," He said, *"You are called to bring laughter to the nations."* After hearing that, I laughed even more.

As I laid out on the grass by the pool, laughing, I suddenly heard voices coming near me. It was the head cook and another woman.

She said, "Excuse me, but this lady here would like prayer for depression to leave. She needs what you have. So, I will leave her here so you can pray for her."

But I wasn't praying for anyone. I was full of laughter and utterly oblivious to everyone and everything. I was out there by the pool, all alone, laughing with a jacket over my eyes to protect myself from the sun.

While I was laughing, the lady began to chuckle, and pretty soon, she started laughing and ended up getting touched with the same joy I had been experiencing. As she laughed, she fell to the ground and laughed harder. After that, we were both rolling around on the grass, laughing.

Then, suddenly, another lady came toward us and said, "Excuse me, can you pray for me? My ears, I have pain in my ears. Can you pray for the pain to go away?" But again, I wasn't praying for anyone. I was laughing.

So, my response was, "What?"

Despite my reaction and laughter, I put my hand on her ears, and suddenly, she exclaimed, "The pain—it is all gone!"

During the trip God kept putting people in my path, and I was excited about what He was doing, which caused me to laugh even more.

Our schedule, while in Africa, included going to minister at a men's prison. The inmates were between the ages of sixteen and twenty-four years old. This was my first time visiting a prison. I felt both apprehension and excitement at the same time. On that day, we saw 300 men give their lives to Christ. Still, I laughed all day long.

Early in the morning on this day, I had spent a lot of time in the presence of God. If I had not spent that time with the Father, I might have been overwhelmed. However, I was overflowing with the joy of the Lord, and it sustained me. No matter what I did throughout the entire day, I could not stop laughing. I would hear or see something that would trigger me to start laughing again and I eventually ended up laughing for 15 hours. I became so full of joy that this now became my new normal. I had a new found joy but wasn't sure what to do with it.

At the beginning of this chapter, I shared a manifestation of food flying out of my mouth. Let me tell you why I believe God did not let me eat that day in South Africa. Two years after this encounter, I was on a different ministry trip in the United States near Chicago. I was with a small group heading to the airport when someone shared a funny story and made a funny face. I began to laugh. The only problem was I had taken a drink of water at the same time too. Unfortunately, I breathed in, and the next thing I knew, I could not get any air. The crazy thing is, right before this, I was laughing and saw a road sign that had the number 23 on it. Immediately I thought of the scripture Psalm 23 (. *"Yea though I walk through the valley of the shadow of death; I will fear no evil."*

I felt it was strange to be thinking of that scripture since everything seemed just fine at the time. Little did I know that scripture would begin to play out twenty minutes later; after drinking the water while laughing in the car. Because I drank water and laughed at the same time, I started to suffocate. I had no air; I could not breathe. I then started to see my whole life pass before me; my family, children, and everything I had ever done flashed before my eyes. I realized that I would die if I didn't get air soon.

Finally, praise God, the pastor driving the car looked over at me in the passenger seat and asked if I was ok. I shook my head to say no and grabbed my chest, so he started violently beating on my back while driving. Up to this point, I hadn't tried to cause a commotion since we were in traffic, and I didn't want to get us all in an accident. Finally, after several moments of stiff blows to my back, my airway opened enough for me to get some air. We stopped at a light, and I opened the door to get an enormous breath of fresh air.

At that moment, I had never been so happy to breathe in the fresh air. Thank goodness I did not suffer any side effects or, even worse, death. I learned a huge lesson that day when you are laughing, don't be eating or drinking because it might kill you. From that day on, if I start to laugh while eating or drinking, I will walk away to get composure or spit my drink or food out. I would rather do that than end up dead due to choking or asphyxiation. So, while reading this book, please don't eat or drink if you laugh. Trust me; it can be hazardous to your health.

As you read this, my prayer is that you will get hit with joy. Because this is all breathed through the Holy Spirit. I speak that over you right now that you too will experience supernatural joy. It will be so uncontrollable that you will not be able to contain it. I pray that pure joy will be your portion.

Godly Lifestyle Activation

God wants you to live in His truth which is based on the Word of God. That will take time for you to learn and go deep into your spirit man rooting out all lies. Here are some activations I want to give you to get you started on your journey.

God's Truth

> ➢ Many people think it is more spiritual to cry rather than laugh. However, the Word of God shows us in His presence is fullness of joy. Let's look at the complete verse.

"You will show me the path of life; In Your presence is fullness of joy; At Your right hand are pleasures forevermore." - Psalm 16:11 NKJV

> ➢ We love to hear our children laugh, so how much more does our Heavenly Father love to listen to His children laugh?

"If a son asks for bread from any father among you, will he give him a stone? Or if he asks for a fish, will he give him a serpent instead of a fish? Or if he asks for an egg, will he offer him a scorpion? If you then, being evil, know how to give good gifts to your children, how much more will your heavenly Father give the Holy Spirit to those who ask Him!" - Luke 11:11-13 NKJV

> ➢ God made this beautiful world for us to enjoy. It is God's will for us to be fruitful in every area of our lives.

"But the fruit of the Spirit is love, joy, peace, long-suffering, kindness, goodness, faithfulness, gentleness, self-control. Against such things there is no law." - Galatians 5:22-23 NKJV

"Let your light so shine before men, that they may see your good works and glorify your Father in heaven." - Matthew 5:16 NKJV

> ➢ You may not feel like laughing, but it becomes a sacrifice to God as you choose to laugh.

"Therefore, by Him let us continually offer the sacrifice of praise to God, that is, the fruit of our lips, giving thanks to His name."
- Hebrews 13:15 NKJV

➤ Laughter and joy can cost you your dignity.

"Then David danced before the Lord with all his might, and David was wearing a linen ephod...'And I will be even more undignified than this and will be humble in my sight."- 2 Samuel 6:14-22 NKJV

➤ Our loving Father gives us laughter and joy as a gift.

"Whoever desires, let him take the water of life freely."
- Revelation 22:17 NKJV

"Thanks be to God for His indescribable gift!" - 2 Corinthians 9:15 NKJV

Your Response to God's Truth

Consider journaling while you read this book. Grab a journal and begin to hear what Holy Spirit is saying to you about laughter in your life.

Begin by writing down the areas where you need a breakthrough. This breakthrough could be in relationships, finances, family, jobs, emotions, thoughts, health, etc.

Then, write the word "JOY" over your list as a declaration that God's joy can not only give you strength but can defeat all attacks of the enemy.

Scriptures for Further Study

Scripture is a great way to be encouraged and help you to start having a conversation on your own with God about this truth of laughter in your personal life. Take time to meditate on these verses and let them speak to your heart.

"He who sits in the heavens shall laugh; The Lord shall hold them in derision." - Psalm 2:4 NKJV

"You will show me the path of life; In Your presence is fullness of joy; At Your right hand are pleasures forevermore." - Psalm 16:11 NKJV

"But the fruit of the Spirit is love, joy, peace, longsuffering, kindness, goodness, faithfulness, gentleness, self-control. Against such there is no law."
- Galatians 5:22-23 NKJV

"And the Spirit and the bride say, "Come!" And let him who hears say, "Come!" And let him who thirsts come. Whoever desires, let him take the water of life freely." - Revelation 22:17 NKJV

"Then he said to them, "Go your way, eat the fat, drink the sweet, and send portions to those for whom nothing is prepared; for this day is holy to our Lord. Do not sorrow, for the joy of the Lord is your strength."
- Nehemiah 8:10 NKJV

CHAPTER TWO

What is Laughter?

When I thought about the question of what laughter was, I thought, what better place to discover clarity than the dictionary? We all have different ideas about what laughter means to us, and our upbringing or cultural background may influence it. You may think it's an act, an emotion, or as some have said, "an inside job." But, according to Webster's Dictionary Online, laughter is all these things and even more. If we don't understand it or know what it means, we could misinterpret it and miss out on its value in our life. What does the word laugh really mean? Let's see.

Laugh means: *to show emotion (such as mirth, joy, or scorn) with a chuckle or explosive vocal sound.* Laughter refers to your spontaneous, unusual, or usually unarticulated sounds, often accompanied by corresponding body movements, in which you express a specific emotion, especially joy or delight. Laughing makes you move! When you start laughing, your body will respond.

Often, we use words in our language without knowing what they mean. And that's when problems can start. To better understand what laughing means, I looked up some other words associated with it. There are many others, but here are the ones I'd like to highlight for you. I want to begin with, "Ha."

According to the Merriam-Webster dictionary, ha is a word that means *joy, surprise, or triumph.* I know that seems simple. When we laugh, we usually say ha, ha, ha, ha. Even when I am writing and wanting to make something funny, what do I write? You guessed it ha, ha, ha. But the most significant thing about ha is that it is universal.

It doesn't matter where I go. If I travel around the United States of America or go to different countries such as China, Europe, or Africa and say, "ha, ha, ha" people will know what I'm doing. They will know I am laughing. It doesn't matter where I am on this planet. Laughing is an inherent gift from God. God made laughter sovereign, and He made you to be filled with joy and to be filled with laughter through the word ha.

Next, we have the word happy. Generally, happy refers to a pleasant feeling of well-being, enjoyment, contentment, or happiness. Pharrell Williams' has a video for the song "Happy" which illustrates that happiness is for everyone. In the music video, everyone from little kids to older adults is dancing to it. When I hear this song in a store, I start moving instinctively. It describes a feeling of well-being that you can feel all through the song. I feel happy every time I hear it.

Joy is defined as *a feeling of great pleasure and happiness*. Joyful refers to something that causes or shows joy. Whenever someone says, "I'm joyful," they describe their feelings; they are excited. The word joyous has a similar meaning to joyful. However, it usually refers to the state of being happy or having a happy nature or mood. When you are joyful, you are joyous, and you feel good about something.

The word glad is defined as *experiencing pleasure, joy, or delight; made happy*. This word describes your good feelings when you think about something special. When you use positive words, you are empowered to accomplish amazing things. Good words evoke a good feeling.

Delight is a word used to describe extreme pleasure about something. Would you like to know who is delighted with you? God! God is delighted with you. In case you didn't know, God has extreme pleasure over you right now. God delights in you, regardless of what is happening inside you, your circumstances, and what your body tells you. Take a minute to meditate on the fact that God delights in you no matter what. It's an amazing thing to know that the Creator of the universe delights in you! What a powerful thought!

The next word is hilarious which means *extremely amusing*. It refers to causing laughter and entertainment that is exceptionally funny. God has given so much to us through the word laugh. Why don't you give it a try? Ha, ha, ha, ha.

Great job! We will be doing this a lot through the book. The best way to learn is by repetition and laughter is truly repetitious.

Now that you've heard some incredible definitions of what laughter means, I'd like to share more good news with you. The benefits of laughing are for everyone, regardless of race, religion, or age. Anyone can reap the benefits of laughter.

Do you want to bring unity and more people together? Would you like your relationship with your family, children, and spouse to be more intimate? Start laughing. You'll be surprised what can happen when you begin to laugh. What a remarkable and contagious gift we have. In a later chapter, you will discover all the fantastic benefits that laughter can bring to your life that will encourage you to laugh more.

Have you ever woken up thinking how difficult your day will be? Then, as you start your day, nothing seems to go as planned, and you begin to think and say out loud "today is going to be a terrible day". When you do this, you have just fulfilled your own prophecy or words. All the negative things you said to yourself have now come true or will come true because of the power of your words. When you speak in a negative way you call those things into existence in your life.

But what would happen if you changed the narrative? What if you got out of bed with a charge inside of you of feeling joy and laughter from the inside out? What if you decided to feel 'happy'? Everything would change.

Let's say you had a bad day, and you lost your job. Instead of feeling down or speaking pessimistically, your response could be laughter. You would not be laughing because it is great news, you would laugh because you know the One that is the source of joy.

After that, if someone says, "you just lost your job," and your response is laughter because you are filled with such peace. It is filled with knowing that source of all joy and where to get it. It is not based on anything in this world, but on who you are. It is because of Christ in you, the hope of glory.

In the same way, people love to hear their little ones laugh, how much more do you think our God enjoys hearing His children laugh? He does. He didn't create this beautiful planet for us to stay unhappy, broken, and sad all the time. Instead, He designed it so we could create, enjoy, and be happy. He made this world a place where we can be joyful and grow in Him. He wanted us to multiply and be fruitful on the earth. He wanted us to replicate Him and that relationship with our families.

So many of us believe that it is more spiritual to be full of tears to be closer to God. That is simply not true. We will have tears but even in that God said that He keeps all our tears in bottles in heaven. He cares for us that much that even our tears mean something to the Lord.

There is a scripture in the book of Ecclesiastes that says, "*...a time to weep and a time to laugh..." Ecclesiastes 3:4 AMP*. Every time we enter God's presence, whether with tears of joy or sadness, we can be joyous. We should be happy as we live in His presence. That is our inheritance.

God says in Psalm 16:11 *NKJV*, *"In Your presence is fullness of joy"*. There should be people who approach us and say, "I don't what it is about you, but you seem so happy." People should want to be around us because we are so happy and full of joy. Laughter and joy are that contagious.

If you want to have more fun in your life, start laughing and watch as people come around you. As you embrace this new truth, He will use joy to change your life and the world around you. Are you ready to be full of contagious laughter and joy?

Joy begins with a smile. Joy is simple. All you must do is try it. When you smile, everything inside you starts anticipating something fun and amazing. Did you know it takes more muscles to frown than to smile? So, start smiling today. You will feel better and those you smile at will feel better.

Godly Lifestyle Activation

God wants you to laugh. He wants you to learn this truth and gift. Let's look at some truths connected to laughter.

God's Truth

➢ While laughter has many healing agents to assist in healing the body, it's also medicine for the soul. A good laugh can do more for us than all the chocolate in the world. I will admit that thought is a bit exaggerated, but it's true that laughter is soul food too. Laughter can transform our emotions for the better. Laughter also makes us more productive in every area of our lives.

"Pleasant words are like a honeycomb, Sweetness to the soul and health to the bones." - Proverbs 16:24 NKJV

➢ When we speak gracious words, they make God happy. Likewise, when we say kind words to everyone around us, God is pleased with us. But when we speak like the world and speak negatively, God doesn't like that.

"The thoughts of the wicked are an abomination to the Lord, But the words of the pure are pleasant." - Proverbs 15:26 NKJV

➢ Words that are spoken at the right time are sweet to God's ears. But they are also sweet to the person that hears them. He gives us the right things to say to someone at precisely the right time. Saying the right words whenever someone needs them pleases us and makes our hearts feel cheerful. It also makes the person we are trying to cheer up feel good.

"A word fitly spoken is like apples of gold in settings of silver." - Proverbs 25:11 NKJV

"A man has joy by the answer of his mouth, and a word spoken in due season, how good it is! - Proverbs 15:23 NKJV

"A man's stomach shall be satisfied from the fruit of his mouth; From the produce of his lips, he shall be filled." - Proverbs 18:20 NKJV

Your Response to God's Truth

The goal with this activation is going to take you out of your comfort zone and into more intentionality about joy. I want you to smile at everyone you meet this week. You may say that is easy, but you would be surprised at how many people do not smile. Your responses will get more challenging as you embrace the new revelation you receive each chapter. I hope after reading this, the value of laughter will change in your life. As you read, let the message of laughter stir you to laugh more and reap the benefits that come with it.

Pray that even as you listen to or read this book, God will come and touch your heart with hilarious joy.

Scriptures for Further Study

"You will show me the path of life; In Your presence is fullness of joy; At Your right hand are pleasures forevermore." - Psalm 16:11 NKJV

"You have put gladness in my heart, more than in the season that their grain and wine increased." - Psalm 4:7 NKJV

"Blessed are you who hunger now, for you shall be filled. Blessed are you who weep now, for you shall laugh." - Luke 6:21 NKJV

"He will yet fill your mouth with laughing, And your lips with rejoicing." - Job 8:21 NKJV

"A time to weep, and a time to laugh; A time to mourn, and a time to dance." - Ecclesiastes 3:4 NKJV

CHAPTER THREE

Laughter is God's Idea

Bill Yount is a Christian author and the founder of Blowing the Shofar Ministries. He shared in an article I read how a few of his ministry friends had a very powerful encounter with joy. I would like to share it with you.

Bill recounted a time when some of his fellow Christians friends wanted to gather for a meal. They hadn't planned on entering God's holy realm of laughter, not even by accident. A few of the couples gathered including a couple they had not seen in many years. Bill mentioned that he is kind of a caveman when it comes to social gatherings and that he was exhausted and felt that he needed a vacation. But he agreed to go to the dinner. He didn't feel very spiritual that day. He was very tired. In fact, he said he "felt spiritually dry and wasn't in the mood to hear how God might be blessing other people" when his head wasn't in the right place, much less his spirit not being in the right place. But, he recalled, "it seemed to begin at the table right after we had eaten."[1] Please take note it happened after they had eaten.

He stated that there came such freedom to share the ups and downs in their lives, as well as in ministry. They weren't doing anything spiritual. They were talking about the mishaps of ministry life. Then they all started

---

[1] While Laughing Uncontrollably, God Told Us, You've Just Entered the Highest Realm of My Glory by Bill Yount (stablerack.com)

laughing, and that is when God said to all of them, *"You just entered into the highest realm of my glory."*

Can you believe that? Wow! What a statement God made to them. When I heard this, I wanted that in my life right then and there. I needed this in my life. How many of you want to enter the highest realm of God's glory? They did it through laughter. That's right, laughter is the key to entering the highest realm of God's glory.

People in that dinner group shared their discouraging times and the bloopers in their ministries. As he and the people talked, they began to experience a type of joy none of them had experienced before, which can only come from God. It was a joy unspeakable. Bill remembered that it offered such freedom to share their ministry stories, and the people he was with suddenly became, even more, real to him. God seemed to untie the heavy yokes that were wrapped around their hearts during their everyday lives.

He said that the joy of the Lord started falling like an avalanche on all of them as he sensed the Lord saying, *"you have just entered into the highest place of fellowship with me."* Bill then mentioned the power of being in fellowship with God and fellowship with another person. He stated, "I believe there was a cleansing spirit as we were in fellowship with one another in the body of Christ."

Bill shared some scriptures as he told this story that I want to share with you to give you an idea of the power of laughter and how laughter is really God's idea.

Jesus desires that your joy be full. He wants you full of joy not full of the world and problems. When you feel the fullness of the world crashing down on you, God will come with laughter as He did in this group of gathering ministers. Jesus said, *"But now I come to You, and these things I speak in the world, that they may have My joy fulfilled in themselves."*- *John 17:13 NKJV*

Laughter fills your life with the power and glory of God. "Laughter is the echo of the vacant grave," is a quote from Mabel Andlers. She explains that laughter is in the empty tomb. In fact, when Kathie Walters was in the Garden Tomb in Israel, she was trying to be very reverent. Then an angel tapped her on the shoulder and spoke to her saying, "He certainly isn't here!" She started laughing and laughing because the angel didn't seem to make an idol of the empty grave.

Laughter is the outward manifestation of being more than a conqueror. God called you to conquer situations that arise in your life. There are times that heaviness can come and almost defeat you, but you can defeat them all with laughter.

Laughter also brings you into the presence and encounter of God. I heard Steve Backlund say one time that "a chronic lack of joy is a representation of an incomplete God encounter. We may not be outrageously joyful every time we're in His presence but if we are never outrageously joyful in His presence we may not be in His presence as much as we thought we were." That is powerful.

According to a study by psychologist Herbert Lefcourt Ph.D. of the University of Waterloo, and Rod Martin, Ph.D., now at the University of Western, Ontario, "stressed out people with a strong sense of humor become less depressed and anxious than those people with a less developed sense of humor." [2]

In the beginning, God created the heavens and the earth, and a few verses later, the Bible explains that He made man in His image. Since God created man, He also created laughter because laughter is in God. I have shown you that from the word of God. Laughter is God's medicine for the body, soul, and spirit. Within His Word, He teaches us how laughter works. There are more than eighty scriptures dedicated to the subject of joy alone. Isn't that amazing? But we rarely hear this taught very much.

Christ lives within you and me. People that don't know Jesus should just be running to be in our presence because we're so joyful everywhere we go not because everything is joyful but because of who is in us. The person of Jesus is joy. Something happens when you release joy. Joy confuses the enemy on all fronts.

Laughing and being filled with joy doesn't seem to be the powerful of activities a person can do. But not according to Kathie Walters. She says

[2] http://www.laughingmatters.org/why-laughter.html

that laughter is like a weapon each believer can use. She says, "I believe that the laughter (God's laughter) brings down that victory into our experience."[3] Laughter gets rid of fear in the heart when activated. Throughout this book, you will be activated, and I am telling you that if you grab hold of joy, it will change your life in ways you never imagined.

When I attended the School of Supernatural Ministry we practiced how to laugh at school. You might wonder why you would need to practice laughing. We all came from different backgrounds and cultures, and they were teaching us a very powerful lesson on joy.

First, one of the leaders shared the importance of joy with the students. He said, "Okay, this is how you do it. You say "ha, ha, he, he, ho, ho." By doing that one little exercise, people began to laugh. I learned a vital lesson that sometimes we need to practice laughing. You may have to initiate it even when you feel nothing worth laughing over. That is okay.

In a message I heard recently, a pastor shared, "The Holy Spirit is the most enthusiastic person you will ever meet in your whole life. He is like Tigger to the power of a million. He is so excited about everything." God really is the happiest person you could ever meet. Tigger is my favorite character. He bounces all over the place and is always happy. Since hearing that message whenever I feel down, I think about the Holy Spirit full of joy like Tigger and it cheers me up.

God wants us to be full of joy every day. That doesn't mean that you live in a false reality or that you never have problems. You will have problems, but you can still have joy and laughter. You can walk in that every single day no matter what is going on in you or around you.

What about people that drink coffee? If you drink coffee, you need it to be stimulated and to be energized, right? Would you believe me if I told you that laughter would give you that same energy? God made your body, and He knows the supernatural energy that you need every day. That energy is called "joy."

While I was finishing my bachelor's degree, I had the opportunity to dive into the topic of laughter at great lengths as I was writing a paper

---

[3] https://elijahlist.com/words/display_word/7670

about laughter. My thesis statement was that laughter is God's medicine for body, soul, and spirit.

Whenever you have a thesis statement in college, you must prove it. So, I set out to prove it. I conducted research and found out fantastic things about laughter. Laughter has been in the church for a long time, and not everybody has really understood it. Some of the people have run from laughter. Some people have even said, "oh my goodness, here come those crazy Christians that are laughing. There's something wrong with them. They're rolling on the floor. There is something wrong with this picture."

According to *Genesis 21:6 NKJV* "...*Sarah said, 'God has made me laugh, and all who hear will laugh with me.'*" She gave birth to a son named Isaac just as God said she would. It was a miracle. In Hebrew, Isaac means "he will laugh, he will rejoice."

This part of the story should encourage you that there is power in a name. Perhaps you have not discovered the meaning of your name. If not, ask God to reveal to you the significance of your name. Identity is found in your name. Jesus knew the power of identity and never backed down from walking in that identity even when He faced ridicule from others.

Let me give you an example of people making a mockery of laughter concerning Jesus. The story in Matthew 9:24 *NKJV* says, *"He said to them, 'Make room, for the girl is not dead, but sleeping. And they ridiculed Him.'"*

Sometimes we think, that laughing is mockery, and in this scripture, it was. In this passage of scripture Jairus, a leader in the synagogue, appears to have suffered a significant loss. He has lost his only child, a 12-year-old girl. Jairus sought out Jesus before and after the girl died and asked Him to come to lay His hands on her and make her well. Jesus agreed. Read the story in Matthew 9:18–19 and Mark 5:21–24.

When Jesus walks into Jairus' house, it looks like He's too late to help. The professional mourners are already there. Everyone thinks the girl is dead. Jesus orders them to leave. He explains the girl is not dead. She is only asleep. These professional mourners laughed at Jesus, showing their loud sadness was only a performance. It's possible they knew Jesus as a healer. But this time, they thought He was too late. But He was right on time. Despite all the ridicule the world gives believers and God's work, He is laughing in heaven because He knows how the story ends. Why? Because laughter is God's idea.

Have you ever read your kids a story, and they couldn't believe what was happening? Yet, you found yourself chuckling inside since you already knew the ending. God laughs at the enemy's plans because what He plans to do can trump everything else.

We can laugh at the enemy when we know that Christ lives within us when we know who we are, and what we have. We can laugh at every situation we face. Psalm 37:13 *NKJV* is a great scripture about the enemy being defeated in laughter. It says, *"The Lord laughs at him for He sees his day is coming."*

God is laughing at the enemy. He scoffs at all the nations of the world. Our God cannot be defeated when laughter is coming out of your mouth over your life. When you have trouble God laughs at the trouble. *"I also will laugh at your calamities." – Proverbs 1:26 NKJV*

God is laughing at the plans of the enemy because He is greater, and He has a bigger plan! Nothing can defeat laughter.

Let your mouth be filled with laughter and your tongue with joy. Psalm 126:2 *NKJV* is a powerful verse about our mouths being filled with laughter and tongues with singing: *"Then our mouth was filled with laughter, And our tongue with singing. Then they said among the nations, 'The Lord has done great things for them.'"*

God is great and I don't know about you, but I would love my mouth to be filled with laughter. When we laugh like the verse says God will do great things for us. What great things do you need God to do for you?

If you are hungry for anything God will fulfill it. If you are not satisfied, He will satisfy your life. If you are weeping over any circumstance in life, you will weep no more. God is with you, my friend. You will laugh as surely as you are weeping, unsatisfied or hungering you will laugh.

Here is the promise for you to stand on. *Luke 6:21 NIV says: "Blessed are you who hunger now; for you shall be satisfied. Blessed are you who weep now; for you will laugh."*

The good news from the Word of God is that God will fill your mouth with laughter and your lips with shouting. Can you imagine shouting for joy and laughing because God has answered your prayers? You will read about these types of things later in this book. You will see people who now have their mouths filled with laughter and joy because of laughter in their lives.

God is faithful to His word and His promises. When you understand the value of joy, everything changes in your life. Laughter is a gift that God gives, and it will change your life. He is a good Father that gives good gifts. Laugh today.

Godly Lifestyle Activation

Laughter is truly God's idea. He wants you to laugh and to help others bring laughter to their lives as well. The truth is it is biblical to laugh! God wants all of us to be able to laugh and to have consistent joy in our lives. He doesn't want us to live stressed, full of dread, worried and in fear. We must work at not letting the enemy have control over our minds, bodies, and souls. We can resist his evil tactics by saying aloud, "I am a son/daughter of the most-high God. I'm God's child. He is in charge. He wants me to be happy. I don't have to give in to feelings of despair all the time. I can make a choice right here, right now, to be happy. I choose it now."

God's Truth

➢ Joy makes up one-third of the Kingdom of God.

"For the kingdom of God is not eating and drinking, but righteousness and peace and joy in the Holy Spirit." - Romans 14:17 NKJV

➢ Joy is a serious matter of God's Kingdom.

"Again, the kingdom of heaven is like treasure hidden in a field, which a man found and hid; and for joy over it, he goes and sells all that he has and buys that field." - Matthew 13:44 NKJV

➢ Laughter is a gift from God.

"You will show me the path of life: in Your presence is fullness of joy: at Your right hand are pleasures for evermore." - Psalm 16:11 NKJV

Your Response to God's Truth

Take one scripture from the Bible about laughter and read and pray it every day this week. Take a few minutes to ask God how this can help you feel His pleasure in a significant way in your life. If you are sick in your body, read the Proverb that says laughter is good medicine.

Take some time this week to laugh three times this week and test it out and see how it affects your mood and body.

Scriptures for Further Study

"If you then, being evil, know how to give good gifts to your children, how much more will your Father who is in heaven give good things to those who ask Him!" - *Matthew 7:11 NKJV*

"The righteous also shall see, and fear, and shall laugh at him." - *Psalm 52:6 NKJV*

"You will show me the path of life; In Your presence is fullness of joy; At Your right hand are pleasures forevermore." - *Psalm 16:11 NKJV*

"You have put gladness in my heart, more than in the season that their grain and wine increased." - Psalm 4:7 NKJV

CHAPTER FOUR

Laughter is Medicine

We've all heard that eating an apple a day will keep the doctor away. If you want to avoid going back to your doctor, I suggest you eat more fruit and vegetables. Ha ha!

When I was in deep depression God told me that laughing every day would keep my depression away. I decided to take it, the laughter, like medicine. Some may want to know how laughter works like medicine.

A good dose of laughter can be good for health. It can change many things in your life, body, emotions, and more. Additionally, laughter helps reduce tension, manage conflict, and bring people closer together.

Laughter indirectly stimulates endorphins which are the body's natural painkillers. Humor also loosens up our minds. Every time we laugh, we can feel the weight of life lifted off our shoulders. Laughter encourages an out-of-the-ordinary way of looking at things.

"Today scientific belief in laughter's effects on health rests largely on the shoulders of Lee Berk, M.D. and Stanley Tan, M.D. both of The Loma Linda School of Medicine in Loma Linda California." They found that "laughter sharpens most of the instruments in our immune systems tool kit."[4] For example, "it activates T-lymphocytes and natural killer cells, both of which help destroy invading microorganisms. Laughter also increases the production of immunity-boosting gamma interferon and

[4] Happily Ever Laughter | Psychology Today

speeds up the production of new immune cells. And it reduces levels of the stress hormone cortisol, which can weaken the immune system."[5]

Let's look at some of the benefits of laughter for your health and well-being. What if there was only one health benefit to laughter? It would be worth it since it is free. Would you believe me if I told you there are over thirty plus benefits of laughter? Would you be inclined to laugh a little more? Hopefully, even while reading these amazing benefits, you will start to increase how much you laugh each day. God made us, and if He says, "laughter is good medicine," there must be some truth to it.

The health benefits of laughter include but aren't limited to:

Laughter helps to lower and regulate blood pressure. Laughing is the fastest way to lower our blood pressure. According to research, humor can reduce systolic blood pressure by about ten points within twenty minutes.[6]

Laughter improves cardiac health. People who are unable to do other types of physical activity due to injury or illness can benefit from laughter as a cardio workout. For example, walking at a slow, moderate pace burns a similar number of calories per hour as jogging.[7]

Laughter prevents heart disease. The effects of laughter on blood vessels and heart muscles have been shown to protect them from the damaging effects of heart disease.[8]

Laughter reduces stress hormones. When you're stressed, your body releases cortisol. Cortisol is known as the stress hormone, it gets a bad rap, but it plays a vital role in the body. Laughter is one of the ways your body regulates cortisol. Laughter increases oxygen intake, stimulating blood circulation and lowering cortisol levels. There is evidence that just the act of laughing, regardless of whether it is humorous, can relieve stress.[9]

---

[5] Happily Ever Laughter | Psychology Today
[6] Paras Hospitals
[7] Laughter - metrohealth (metrohealthdc.org)
[8] Study Shows Laughter Reducing Heart Disease Risk - Good News Network
[9]https://www.mayoclinic.org/healthy-lifestyle/stress-management/in-depth/stress-relief/art-20044456

"Laughter triggers the release of endorphins, the body's natural feel-good chemicals." Endorphins are our bodies natural painkillers. Laughter releases endorphins, which can help ease chronic pain and make you feel good.[10]

Laughter increases the release of endorphins and dopamine. Laughter increases your intake of the oxygen-rich air. And it also stimulates your heart and muscles and releases endorphins into your body. Endorphins give you a feeling of happiness.[11]

Laughter works your abs. It has been scientifically proven that laughter can help tone your abs. This is because the muscles in your stomach contract and expand when you laugh, like when you exercise your abs. At the same time, the muscles you do not use to laugh are relaxing.[12]

When people laugh, their levels of gamma-interferon and T-cells are increased in the body. These cells work to fight disease and eliminate tumors.[13]

Laughter boosts T-cells to help fight off illness. Your immune system contains specialized T-cells waiting to be used. When you laugh, your T-cells begin to fight off illness immediately. Next time you feel a cold coming on, just laugh.[14]

Laughter increases blood flow and oxygenation to the cells and organs. We suddenly increase our oxygen levels when we laugh deeply, stimulating our heart, lungs, brain, and other muscles. As a result of this stimulation, cells regenerate, organs remain healthy, and it is a low-impact activity.[15]

Laughter increases memory, intelligence, and creativity. In addition, laughter increases oxygen to the brain, which improves memory.[16]

---

[10] Laughter is the Best Medicine - HelpGuide.org
[11] How Does Laughter Can Relieve Stress | USAHS
[12] https://www.gaiam.com/blogs/discover/7-health-benefits-of-laughter
[13] How do B cells and T cells work to fight disease? - POZ
[14] Scientific benefits of laughter for physical, mental and social health- FactDr
[15] Stress relief from laughter? It's no joke - Mayo Clinic
[16] https://iheartintelligence.com/laughter-increases-memory-abilities/

Laughter prevents cancer. Cancer and other diseases can be prevented or treated by increasing positive thinking and happy feelings that support the healing process.[17]

Laughter enhances mood. Laughing can relieve depression and anxiety and will help you feel better overall.[18]

Laughter helps with respiratory infections, and common colds can be inhibited and decreased. When you laugh, you produce more IgA (immunoglobulin A), which fights upper respiratory tract infections.[19]

Laughter impacts the limbic system, which can affect your mental health. "The limbic system is involved in all emotions, including laughter…"[20]

Laughter stimulates your whole body to feel energized and refreshed. Laughing increases oxygen consumption and releases endorphins, the feel-good hormones that make you happy.[21]

Laughter burns calories. In fact, "laughing for an average of 15 minutes a day burns around 40 calories." Your metabolism increases as your heart rate rises, so you will still burn calories even after you stop laughing.[22]

Laughter boosts mood and confidence. You become less defensive, more spontaneous, and less inhibited when you laugh.[23]

Laughter helps you get through hard times. In addition to relieving tension, laughter allows us to maintain a positive outlook. Having breathing room enables us to see the bright side of difficult situations, giving us a more positive perspective.[24]

[17] The power of laughter for cancer patients | CTCA (cancercenter.com)
[18] Laughter May Be The Cure To Depression, Anxiety And Much More - Gilmore Health
[19] Laughter Therapy - An Effective Treatment - nmmra.org
[20] Why Laughter Is Good For Mental Health (laughteronlineuniversity.com)
[21] 9 Surprising Benefits of Laughter You Need to Know (lifehack.org)
[22] Laughing Burns Calories! – Passion (psu.edu)
[23] Laughter is the Best Medicine - HelpGuide.org

[24] 9 Benefits of Laughter and What You Need To Know (amindbend.com)

Laughter soothes tension and relaxes muscles. As a result, laughing can help with circulation and muscle relaxation, reducing some of the physical signs of stress.[25]

Laughter enhances creativity and problem-solving skills. By laughing regularly, we will be able to think creatively, solve problems, be alert, and remember more. In addition, having positive emotions helps us organize information, store it in the brain for a more extended period, and retrieve it faster later.[26]

Laughter raises self-esteem, hope, optimism, energy, and vigor.[27]

As you can see, laughter has some great healing benefits to the body, mind, and emotions. There is much to be gained from you adding laughter to your life.

Studies show that people with more positive emotions exhibit higher psychological and physiological well-being levels, including "confidence, optimism, self-efficacy, likability…sociability, activity, and energy," In addition, when faced with challenges and stress, they are more flexible and effectively able to act.[28] Let's look at more benefits.

Laughter improves interpersonal interactions and relationships. A good laugh also enables you to create a better bond with friends and family. It helps you in so many ways.[29]

Laughter attracts others. Women say they want someone who will make them laugh. But men want someone they can make laugh.[30]

Laughter enhances teamwork. In jobs where people work in teams, laughter strengthens the ties between the members and, at the same time, reduces stress.[31]

Laughter helps to defuse conflict. According to research, when people laugh and see the humor in a conflict situation, they are more likely to

[25]Stress relief from laughter? It's no joke - Mayo Clinic
[26]The Power of Humor in Ideation and Creativity | Psychology Today
[27]Positive Emotions and Your Health | NIH News in Health
[28] bul-1316803.pdf (apa.org)
[29]Seven ways laughter can improve your well-being | Wu Tsai Neurosciences Institute (stanford.edu)
[30]People Will Like You If You Make Them Laugh | Psychology Today
[31]Why laughter can make you more productive at work (cnbc.com)

switch from convergent thinking (seeing one possibility) to divergent thinking (seeing other possibilities and ideas that may resolve the conflict).[32]

Laughter promotes bonding and strengthens relationships. Health and happiness are closely related to the quality of your relationships, and laughter binds people together.[33]

Laughter increases productivity at work. Happy people work harder. If someone is happy, they may be able to accomplish in one hour what it takes someone less happy to achieve in an hour and twenty minutes.[34]

Laughter helps people take less time off from work. Laughter fires up your stress response, increases your heart rate, and lowers your blood pressure. Lower stress levels help in reducing absenteeism.[35]

Laughter shifts a negative perspective. David H. Rosen, a psychologist, suggests that humor inhibits the formation of negative thoughts and encourages the formation of positive ones.[36]

Laughter increases your love relationship. Of course, we can stay together through love, but shared laughter makes our relationships fun and helps them last longer.[37]

Laughter heals your soul. When you choose to laugh, you embrace the joy of the Lord, and that decision positively influences not only your soul, but also your body and spirit.

Laughter inspires hope. Texas A&M University research shows that humor may significantly increase a person's level of hope.[38]

Laughter helps extend your life. Laughing regularly makes you happier and reduces stress, so you live longer.

---

[32] Managing Conflict with Humor - HelpGuide.org
[33] Managing Conflict with Humor - HelpGuide.org
[34] Why laughter can make you more productive at work (cnbc.com)
[35] 8 Amazing Facts About Humor in the Workplace - Article (intuit.com)
[36] Humor Can Increase Hope, Research Shows -- ScienceDaily
[37] How Laughter Brings Us Together (berkeley.edu)
[38] Humor Can Increase Hope, Research Shows -- ScienceDaily

Laughter helps with skin conditions. When individuals with eczema laugh repeatedly, their complexions improve. For allergy sufferers, laughing helps shrink their welts.[39]

As you can see the benefits are hard to ignore of how laughter impacts your life for good.

When your car breaks down, where do you go? Some people go to their car manual first to check to see if the answer is there. If they can't fix their problem, then they go to a mechanic to see if they can diagnose the problem you're having with your vehicle. We should do the same thing when we have problems that we don't know how to fix. We should go to the author of our lives, God Himself, *and* read the manual, also known as the Bible first, instead of looking for our own solutions or just worrying and complaining.

Even on TV, we see all these drugs have terrible side effects, and some even include death. Why would anyone want death for themselves? Instead, we should go to God and ask Him to care for us. We should learn to trust that He is the Great Physician and that He is our ultimate source of healing.

When we laugh, we are confusing the plans of the enemy. We can sit there laughing, and the enemy might say, "I just came to steal, kill, and destroy, and you are laughing?"

We know deep in our hearts that we have a bigger truth and that we can always turn to God for help, no matter what we are going through. So, with laughter, we are saying back to the enemy, "I'm partnering with my Father in heaven. He has control over my life, not you! This is what He is doing in heaven right now. He's laughing at the plans of the enemy, so I am going to laugh with Him as His precious, chosen, and beloved child. I'm going to become like a laughing hyena."

In the book of James 1:2-8 *NIV*, it says:

> *"Consider it pure joy, my brothers and sisters, whenever you face trials of many kinds, because you know that the testing of your faith produces*

---

[39]Can laughter cure illness? | HowStuffWorks

perseverance. Let perseverance finish its work so that you may be mature and complete, not lacking anything. If any of you lacks wisdom, you should ask God, who gives generously to all without finding fault, and it will be given to you. But when you ask, you must believe and not doubt, because the one who doubts is like a wave of the sea, blown and tossed by the wind. That person should not expect to receive anything from the Lord. Such a person is double-minded and unstable in all they do."

Think about it for a minute. How many of you laughed the last time you experienced a trial? The last time the pressure was on did you laugh? Did you even feel like laughing? Probably not. But that is the best time to laugh. Be honest with yourself. If you did laugh through a tribulation, praise God. If you didn't, what can you learn and teach yourself to do the next time a hardship comes upon you?

Remember that you have every opportunity to laugh whenever you're going through trials.

When you laugh, you are carefree. When you laugh you put the enemy on the run. When you laugh you begin to change the circumstance. When you laugh you gain strength. When you laugh you relax as you respond to feeling joyful.

So, let's give this a try. As a point of contact, put your hand on wherever part of your body that is hurting and then do what God asks you to do; just start laughing. So, you're taking the negative, which is your sickness, and turning it into something positive through laughter. You might say, "Yeah, but I don't feel it." It's ok. Your body is responding. Or you might say, "I don't want it to be fake. I don't want it to sound like something I am making up."

You're not making it up. I promise it is a gift. Put your hand wherever the painful part of your body is and start thinking about God and just start laughing.

Have you ever watched the movie "Patch Adams"? Patch Adams was more than just a movie starring Robin Williams. "Patch" Adams founded the Gesundheit Institute[40]. During the 1970s, he enrolled in medical

---

[40] https://www.patchadams.org

school. He genuinely wanted to see people happy and didn't see them as medical projects. Instead, he demonstrated true compassion for those who were ill. And sometimes, he did it in the most unconventional way through laughter.

As a result, he started dressing up as a clown. In those days, people in the medical field were horrified by what he was doing! They were saying to him, "*What are you doing? By treating laughter as medicine, you mock the medical field!*"

But he knew something. He knew that joy was medicine. When people began to laugh, their health started improving. He was not well known until many years later when the movie "Patch Adams" came out. Eventually, the medical field began to talk about how medicine and laughter go together. As you read this book, whatever is going on in your body, whatever pain you may be experiencing, I want you to start to laugh even if all you can do is say, "ha, ha, ha" as your first step to laughing.

You don't need to let your circumstances dictate your attitude. With so much destruction, it is easy for anyone to get depressed. However, God has the answer.

A few years ago, I watched a movie and heard God speak to me. It was as if the Lord said, "*If you look at the problem, you will not see the solution. Look at Me instead. Then you will be able to see the solution too.*"

Maybe this doesn't mean anything to anyone else, but it's clear to me. When we focus on our circumstances, we can only see our problem. But if we start laughing, our mood will change, and we will get clarity.

Psalm 16:11 *NKJV* says, "*You will show me the path of life; In Your presence is fullness of joy; At Your right hand are pleasures forevermore.*" That is such a precious promise from God. In His presence is what? The fullness of sorrow? No! It is fullness of joy!

As I have done the research, I have also discovered some fantastic statistics. For example, the University of Maryland Medical Center conducted a study that showed laughter increases the production of antibodies that protect us from disease. In addition, cortisol levels are reduced by laughter. Using ultrasound, researchers found that due to artery dilation, blood flow increased by twenty-two percent during laughter and decreased by thirty-five percent during mental stress.[41] This is because the body's natural painkillers, endorphins, are released when we laugh. After researching and finding out all this information, I realized that God has given us everything we need.

We go to doctors, and I'm not negating doctors, but I've got a new pill for you, and it's called "laughter." Start incorporating it into your daily routine and see what happens. It might just make you well.

The Bible says we must become like children to enter the kingdom of God. He said, *"Truly I tell you, unless you change and become like little children, you will never enter the kingdom of heaven."- Matthew 18:3 NIV*. So often, we forget what it is like to have the faith of a child. Children don't have to see things to believe that they exist. It's kind of like the way they believe in Santa Claus. They don't have to see the North Pole or Santa Claus to believe that they are both real to them. In the same way, they don't have to see Jesus to know that He is real, alive, and present in the world.

So often, you see kids laughing and being carefree in their lives. Whenever they are laughing and playing, even when they fall and get hurt, what do we do as parents? We try to come to them and meet them at their level, no matter how old they are, with a smile on our faces, and we say, "Don't worry about it. You're ok. You're fine. Just shake it off. Let's just laugh it off. It'll pass." Right? We teach our children to laugh. We are not doing it just for ourselves. We are teaching our children to laugh instead of crying all the time.

Many in the world are crying out for joy. The term L.O.L. means laugh out loud. You see it posted a lot on social media. People all over the world are searching for this in their lives. Many people have even started something called laughing yoga. Have you heard of the term laughing yoga? A Hindu doctor in India had a dream about how laughter is good medicine. Oh, wait that comes directly out of the Bible from the book of Proverbs. This doctor woke up and concluded that laughter works like

[41] University Of Maryland School Of Medicine Study Shows Laughter Helps Blood Vessels Function Better -- ScienceDaily

medicine. He decided to gather all his patients together, and told them, "We are going to laugh because I was told it is good medicine." And so, he did. He gathered his patients together. As they laughed and giggled, they quacked at each other like ducks. Seriously! They would make funny faces, laugh, and tell each other jokes. They did anything under the sun to make each other laugh.

Well, guess what happened? It gained momentum all over the world as the word got out people were feeling better and even getting healed, so they decided to call it laughing yoga. The key to their healing is laughter.

Laughing truly is good medicine not because a doctor had a dream but because the God of the universe designed you that way from birth. If you suffer from any sickness in your body, take this in today because it will transform your life. Today, there are more than 20,000 laughing yoga clubs spread across 110 countries. People are paying hundreds to thousands of dollars to learn how to laugh. God has given us this free natural gift, and people are paying to learn how to use it. However, not everyone is experiencing the benefits of laughter and are desperately in need of joy.

According to the USO, there is a staggering statistic concerning suicide in our military in the United States. "In 2021, research found that 30,177 active-duty personnel and veterans who served in the military after 9/11 have died by suicide - compared to the 7,057 service members killed in combat in those same twenty years. That is a military suicide rate four times higher than deaths that occurred during military operations. For military families and parents, whose active duty loved one already sacrifices so much to protect our freedom, this trend is extremely troubling."[42] We know that suicide doesn't just affect the military in our country, but people everywhere; in fact, many of us probably have either experienced or know someone who has experienced the suicide of a loved one.

I heard a speaker share that one of the leading causes of death worldwide is suicide. I was shocked. With all the diseases, wars, crime and

[42] Military Suicide Rates Are at an All-Time High; Here's How We're Trying to Help · United Service Organizations (uso.org)

other things that threaten people daily, it turns out that he was correct; suicide is one of the main leading causes of death. Nearly 800,000 people die by suicide in the world each year. To put that into perspective, that is one suicide death every 40 seconds. It is the second leading cause of death among fifteen- to twenty-four-year-olds in the world. Did you also know that depression is the leading cause of disability in the world?[43]

What if we had a joy and laughter revolution? What kind of dent could we make in those staggering statistics by spreading joy and laughter that comes straight from the heart of the Father? It is something that we need to make a priority I believe. After reading about all the benefits of laughter, I believe teaching others to laugh is not only imperative for people's physical health but also can do miracles for those who are struggling mentally and potentially save lives.

When have you needed joy? Did you go to a counselor? Are you currently taking antidepressants? There is nothing wrong with seeking counseling or taking medicine. I would say, add laughter, even if it's for a minute a day, and see if you start to feel better naturally. I am thankful for medicine when I need it, but I am also grateful when I don't have to take it anymore.

Shortly after learning about all the physical benefits of laughter, I discovered a very practical way to use laughter to solve a problem I would routinely experience when getting my blood drawn. Whenever it was time to get any type of blood work done, my veins seemed to play this "hide and seek" game with the lab nurse. My veins would run away, and the process could often be a long and painful one. Based on the research that proved laughter increases blood flow, I decided to just laugh out loud when I had to have blood drawn. Guess what? It worked! My veins didn't run and the process of getting blood drawn is now easy and virtually painless; all because of laughter.

You may say, "I can't laugh if I don't feel it, I don't have it, I can't make it up." I love it when people say that to me. It makes me smile because I used to be in the same spot myself. I know they genuinely believe it when

---

[43] Suicide Statistics and Facts – SAVE

they say, "I don't want to fake it. I don't want it to sound plastic." Then I ask them questions. Are you fake? Are you plastic? God made you, and He says in *Psalm 126:2 NIV*, *"Our mouths were filled with laughter, our tongues with songs of joy. Then it was said among the nations, 'The Lord has done great things for them.'"*

This is a gift that God has given you. But He's asking you today, what will you do with My gift? Because I promise it will transform your life if you accept it! Maybe you are thinking but you don't even know the pain I am in now. Did you know that your body cannot process joy and stress simultaneously? When stressed, you are all tense; your muscles and blood vessels are tense. When you laugh, your blood vessels open; it opens up everything in your body.

Laughter can protect you from getting sick. Even though the germs are out there, laughing every day can naturally help you fight those germs. Therapeutic laughter has helped so many people in hospitals around the country. For example, in New York, they have something called the Big Apple Circus[44]. People come into the hospitals dressed up as clowns, and they just start laughing. They bring joy and fun to the people staying in the hospital. They get the patients to start laughing, and suddenly, the patient's bodies start responding to the laughter in positive ways. There is something so powerful when we have joy in our lives. Laughter is good for our souls. Even laughing for five to ten minutes per day can benefit us. It's amazing how much changes with laughter.

---

[44] The Healing Benefits of Humor and Laughter - Whole Health Library (va.gov)

Godly Lifestyle Activation

The enemy knows that if he can steal our joy, he can get our strength. There is great power in joy. God tells us not to sorrow; "for the joy of the Lord is your strength." You are stronger than you know.

Ask Holy Spirit to highlight people to you that may be struggling with depression or suicidal thoughts. Ask Him to show you how to impart a Spirit of Joy to them. Then laugh for them as intercession and laugh with them to bring them healing

God's Truth

➤ When you allow yourself to laugh even when you don't feel like it, you will start to feel lighter and less tense. You will relax more and be able to think more clearly.

"For the kingdom of God is not eating and drinking, but righteousness and peace and joy in the Holy Spirit." - Romans 14:17 NKJV

➤ When you get a prescription from the doctor, you take your pills and expect to get better. But you have a "pill" already inside you, and you can start taking God's medicine first. If God made our bodies, then He knows what they need.
God said in His Word, that laughter is like medicine. When you laugh it will heal areas in your life that need healing. God wants your heart to be merry so that your spirit it not broken and dry.

"A merry heart does good, like medicine, but a broken spirit dries the bones." - Proverbs 17:22 NKJV

"But he who is of a merry heart has a continual feast." - Proverbs 15:15 NKJV

➢ God has given you a physical gift—something within your own body. When you laugh, even when you don't feel like laughing, your body responds.

"A merry heart makes a cheerful countenance. But by sorrow of the heart the spirit is broken." - Proverbs 15:13 NKJV

➢ When you laugh, your body releases endorphins and serotonin, natural painkillers.

"I know that nothing is better for them than to rejoice..."
- Ecclesiastes 3:12 NKJV

Your Response to God's Truth

According to Stanford University researcher Dr. William Fry, one minute of laughter is equivalent to ten minutes on a rowing machine. While some say this is an urban myth, there is no doubt in other scientific studies that laughter is so good for your health and well-being. So, it's time to laugh! It's time to take your life out of mediocre joy into extravagant laughter.

I would like to encourage you to start your week by laughing for one minute. Next, laugh for three minutes. Make sure you laugh so others can hear you - no quiet laughing! Call or meet with a friend and laugh together for five minutes.

➢ What comes to mind after you smile intentionally to someone?
➢ How did you feel after three minutes of laughing?
➢ How did others react when they heard you laughing?
➢ If you need healing in your body, lay your hands on the area that needs healing and laugh over it every day.

Scriptures for Further Study

"For the kingdom of God is not eating and drinking, but righteousness and peace and joy in the Holy Spirit." - Romans 14:17 NKJV

"He who sits in the heavens shall laugh; the Lord shall hold them in derision." - Psalm 2:4 NKJV

"A merry heart makes a cheerful countenance, but by sorrow of the heart the spirit is broken." - Proverbs 15:13 NKJV

"Then he said to them, "Go your way, eat the fat, drink the sweet, and send portions to those for whom nothing is prepared; for this day is holy to our Lord. Do not sorrow, for the joy of the Lord is your strength." - Nehemiah 8:10 NKJV

CHAPTER FIVE

Laughter Is Spiritual Warfare

I attended a prophetic class being taught at my church a while back. To my surprise, the pastor was talking about hyenas. It shouldn't have been a surprise as God is good at setting us up to hear the truth He wants to convey.

Remember I mentioned that horrible nickname, Kristina, Kristina the laughing hyena that I was called years earlier? When I heard the pastor talking, I was naturally interested in what he had to say. He taught about the prophetic and how we can learn to discern what is taking place in the natural realm if we pay attention to what we see in the spiritual world. And the opposite is also necessary.

Imagine if we could see what is happening in the spiritual world. In that case, we could discern better how to navigate what is happening in our daily lives since we live in the natural world. He then illustrated this point with a few animals that had great vision to see in the dark, like the owl and the hyena. He shared how hyenas can see at night, which gives them an advantage over their prey. He then explained how in the prophetic world, if we know what is happening in the spiritual realm, we too can have an advantage over our enemy.

At the same time, other animals can't see at night and are at a disadvantage to what is happening around them. God can show us what the enemy is doing in the spiritual realm, so we know how to contend for our breakthrough.

The pastor then asked the class, "Do you know why hyenas laugh?"

No one in the class knew. I surely didn't know but was very curious given my history with the horrible nickname.

Finally, the pastor replied, "When they laugh, they confuse their prey, and they can pounce on and kill it."

I saw the connection. My spirit man leaped for joy inside. I now saw the power in my name, being teased and the laughter. Yes, I wanted to laugh. When we laugh, we confuse the plans of the enemy. The enemy says, "Look at them laughing. I came to steal, kill, destroy, and they're laughing?"

Yes. Yes. We are to tell him, "You have no power over us!"

We are laughing because we are partnering with our Father in heaven. We have power when we start laughing at the plans of the enemy. For years I resisted and hated this nickname but God, today, has turned it for my good. I am becoming like a laughing hyena.

You can laugh at your adversary too no matter what your situation is. Whether you have a sickness or are facing the biggest challenge of your life, you can laugh at the enemy. Even though he comes to steal, kill, and destroy, we can laugh because we know that there is a more profound truth and power at work.

As a child of God, you can partner with your heavenly Father and confuse the enemy with your laughter.

I now saw laughter as a great weapon against the attacks of the enemy in my life.

God's Word tell us that the weapons of our warfare are not carnal but mighty in pulling down strongholds. We have many weapons and laughter is one of them.

Remember Psalm 2:4 says that God "sits in the heavens and laughs" at the plans of the enemy. Another verse says that we "sit in heavenly places" with God. So, if you and I sit with God in heavenly places we laugh with Him, thus we laugh at the enemy also! Don't ever forget that laughter confuses the enemy and God gets all the glory.

This world is in the midst of a spiritual warfare conflict. You may not see it or forget it is even there. However, the enemy would love nothing more than to leave us with a feeling of discouragement and defeat in our minds. As a believer in a dark world, you will face obstacles and attacks. However, we are victorious. We do not have to let the enemy win, despite his cruel attacks. In His Word, God reminds us to be aware of Satan's schemes and to live alert in this world.

Think about the spiritual battles you are facing right now. One of the best weapons we have against the enemy is joy. Because "the joy of the Lord is your strength," the enemy wants to steal it from you. So, we can choose to be joyful and resist the enemy even though it doesn't make sense to the world.

If you have any pain in your body, I want you to test out your body right now because I believe that God is healing some people as you have been reading this book. For example, there is somebody with a lower back problem. Just move your back around. God is already touching you. Somebody has pain in their ribs. If that, is you, go ahead and start laughing. Remember that laughter is spiritual warfare. Could you test it out right now? How are your lower back and ribs doing now? Thank you, Jesus, for your healing!

I pray that God radically deals with your heart concerning joy and that you get hit with extravagant joy when you least expect it and that you have days of joy. I pray that you will never leave that place of happiness. I pray that you will be full of joy everywhere you go. Because of Jesus and His love, you can walk into a sad situation and let God strengthen you to see the joy amidst the sadness. Let the joy of the Lord be your strength, and let's start laughing.

So, for the next minute, I want you to laugh. I want you to see those situations right now, and I want you to start laughing for the next minute.

God woke you up this morning because He still has a plan and purpose for your life. He woke you up to do something incredible with your life. The joy in your life will change the things in your heart and you can have joy as a new normal. I prophesy that over you that as you read this book, that joy will become your new normal.

Someone once told me that I was called to prophetic intercession. When I heard this about my life, I ran the other way because I didn't want anything to do with it. The only type of intercession I had seen growing up looked like a lot of hard work, and people never looked like they were enjoying themselves. However, that belief system was about to be radically changed.

Shortly after I had arrived home from my ministry trip, I felt the joy start to disappear. It didn't help with so many negative situations still looming in my life. I could feel depression knocking on my door. It wasn't long before things began stealing my joy. My mind was wandering, and my gaze shifted away from God. I was preoccupied with these negative situations and problems.

When we focus too much on sickness or family matters it is easy to become discouraged. When you focus on overdue bills that look pink or red you can get overwhelmed. You never want to be in the red area of your finances. Finances are one of the major stressors of life that build up pressure in your life that can cause you to explode at your friends, family, and even at work at the wrong times. I was feeling these pressures as I came back, and they were stealing my joy.

I couldn't understand how I could lose the supernatural joy I had found in South Africa that quickly. I had bills piling up and family issues I was carrying which all caused me to feel overwhelmed as a single mom. Trying to wear both hats in the household can take a toll on a person.

I will never forget the day I prayed as I held some documents in my hands, many of which represented the current problems I was facing. I was in intercession, or so I thought. While I was walking back and forth, wringing my hands, I said, "Oh God, help me." But to be honest, I was complaining more than anything else. That is when the Lord said to me, "Stop and lay your problems down."

I told God, "Don't you see these documents? I need help. I need a breakthrough." He again said, "Lay your troubles down." So reluctantly, I finally laid them down. Then, I could not believe what He asked me to do next.

He told me to laugh over my problems.

I said, "God, you want me to laugh? I must be hearing things!"

Again, I heard Him say, "Laugh over your problems."

The bills were still staring at me, especially those in the red and pink colors. I think people print things in different colors in order of importance. When we get red colors on our bills, we know they are long past due. So, even though I didn't feel like laughing, I began to say, "ha, ha, ha."

Seriously, I was not excited, nor did I feel joy or happiness. I believe I was crying at the time, too.

Again, God said, "I want you to laugh over your problems." So, I started to laugh again.

Then I began to jump on my problems. I realized the more I laughed, the better I felt. I felt my mood shift from sadness to joy. I started to belly laugh just like I had in South Africa. This time, I was in my own home, with no one around, and I fell to the floor and continued to laugh. I laughed and laughed over my problems as I lay there rolling and laughing. I was so full of joy. No one was there telling funny jokes. No one laid hands on me. I had just entered into intercession in a whole new way. This time, it wasn't hard. I laughed for over an hour. Time flew by. By the time I finished, God had already started working on my behalf.

The Lord spoke to me again and said, "You got more done in that hour than you could ever have gotten done by complaining for eight hours."

I could not believe it. I looked at my phone just to see the time but instead noticed that God had already resolved one of my pressing concerns. I knew I was going to be ok.

I said, "Lord, teach me! I want to know how to keep my joy."

You might be thinking that this type of laughter might be fine for me because it was a gift God gave to me. The amazing truth is that joy is a gift for everyone, no matter what we may be dealing with or going through.

When I found out that intercession could be fun, my first reaction was, "Sign me up!"

If you have gotten your focus off the Lord, put your eyes back on Him. Lift your eyes and see His goodness. The joy of the Lord is your strength. It is He who will help you just like He helped strengthen me so I could run faster than ever before.

Right now, I want you to experience a spiritual warfare encounter. If you don't know how to laugh, I want you to say, "Ha, ha, he, he, ho, ho."

I don't want you to laugh quietly. I want you to laugh with all your heart and to really relax your body. I want you to laugh out loud.

In your heart or in your mind's eye, I want you to see the daily obstacles that you face. I want you to see all those mountains in front of you like financial lack, broken relationships, and people who need to be healed. Maybe it's you that needs to be healed. Laugh over it. Laugh until you feel better. I want you to enter a time of spiritual warfare.

First, start laughing over any situation you're facing, even if you think it's ridiculous to laugh. Then you can laugh over the call that will happen in your life through God's almighty power. I want you to see all those situations, and I want you to laugh over them for the next minute. Yes, it may not make any sense to you, but God is moving on your behalf in mighty ways that you can't even imagine, just by letting go and laughing.

In the book of James, it says, *"...count it all joy when you go through trials and tribulations..."* Take a moment to reflect on the last difficulty you faced. How many times did you laugh or feel joyful? As you apply the revelation and everything that this book shows you to your own life, I declare that you will start seeing these truths working for you by the end of today.

Let me show you an example of laughter as spiritual warfare.

During my first year as a student at the School of Ministry, we had many guest speakers. A man was preaching, and his wife was in the front row laughing, I realized at that moment I was struggling with a religious spirit I didn't know I possessed. The entire time the man spoke, his wife laughed. I was judging her, thinking, "I cannot believe how rude she is. Her husband is preaching, and she is making so much noise."

What I didn't know at the time was she was interceding for all of us to be able to receive their message. She was changing the atmosphere with her laughter. What looked like foolishness to me was mighty spiritual warfare. I also noticed that they were both so happy. I had no concept of the joy they were carrying at the time. To be honest, I didn't understand them at all. But that all changed after I had my encounter a year later in South Africa. Once I realized that they were full of joy, I wanted to be filled with as much joy as they were filled with because they had learned a secret that I was finally starting to see for myself. It's a gift so valuable money cannot buy. Laughter.

There are a lot of reasons each of us can draw on to not be happy. The world is looking like an evil mess. Turmoil is on every side. People seem very discouraged. There is a lot of sickness. I remember in my own life a time when multiple problems piled on top of me. I could have been really depressed at the time because I owed more than $50,000 in medical bills, my car had been stolen and I was sick. But I wasn't, because of laughter.

When we find out that God has given us the amazing gift of laughter, we realize it can drastically change our lives for the better. Whatever you are going through right now, I want you to laugh over it. No matter what your problem is, God is still bigger.

Godly Lifestyle Activation

One of the best weapons we have to battle stress, depression, anxiety, and fear is laughter. The Bible says, "For though we walk in the flesh, we do not war according to the flesh. For the weapons of our warfare are not carnal but mighty in God for pulling down strongholds, casting down arguments and every high thing that exalts itself against the knowledge God, bringing every thought into captivity to the obedience of Christ, and being ready to punish all disobedience when your obedience is fulfilled." (II Corinthians 10:3-6 *NKJV*) Laughter is one such weapon!

God's Truth:

➤ God causes us to laugh at those who would want to cause us destruction. The enemy doesn't get to just run around in your life without God doing something.

"The Lord shall laugh at him, for he sees his day is coming."
- Psalm 37:13 NKJV

➤ We can rejoice, for there is nothing better for us to do.

"They will make war on the Lamb, and the Lamb will conquer them, for He is Lord of lords and King of kings, and those with Him are called and chosen and faithful." - Revelation 17:14 NKJV

➤ We are with God as His children, whom He loves, and we are chosen and faithful to Him.

"Submit yourselves therefore to God. Resist the devil, and he will flee from you." - James 4:7 NKJV

Your Response to God's Truth

Make a list of the top three lies that have influenced you over the past month. Then laugh over each one. Here are some examples of common lies:

- ➤ I must get approval from others.
- ➤ I have to be perfect at everything I do.
- ➤ Everything has to be exactly how I want it.
- ➤ I will never be good enough.

Lay down your problems and laugh over them. Make the choice. Be obedient, put your problems in God's hands, and rejoice that He is faithful.

Scriptures for Further Study

"He who sits in the heavens shall laugh; the Lord shall hold them in derision." – Psalm 2:4 NKJV

"He will yet fill your mouth with laughing, and your lips with rejoicing" – Job 8:21 NKJV

"A merry heart does good, like medicine, but a broken spirit dries the bones." – Proverbs 17:22 NKJV

"You have turned my mourning into dancing; You have put off my sackcloth and clothed me with gladness." - Psalm 30:11 NKJV

CHAPTER SIX

Laughter is Contagious

R emember how I shared with you earlier in this book that my life was never the same when I returned from South Africa? Right after I came home, my children, who were ten and thirteen at the time, noticed me being happy. I was a single mom, and my children had never seen me that happy continuously. As soon as I walked through the front door, my children looked at me and said, "What happened to you?"

I asked them what they were talking about because I wasn't sure what they meant. Finally, they said, "You're just so happy! We have never seen you this happy!"

I told them, "I got hit with the Lord's joy in South Africa."

They told me, "Mom, we don't know who you are anymore. You're just so happy.

When our children can tell we have gone from angry, depressed people to someone filled with joy and laughter in our lives, they don't keep quiet about it. When our children can tell that there is a huge difference in us that they have never seen before, they notice and make sure we know it.

What would our world look like if all people were happy? Let's use the movie, *Mary Poppins* as an analogy for contagious laughter. Let me explain.

One morning after I got back from Africa, I was making breakfast. While I was scrambling some eggs, suddenly, my thoughts turned to the classic Disney movie *Mary Poppins* and the song from the film *"I Love to Laugh."* I knew God was speaking to me.[45]

He asked me, "Do you remember Uncle Albert from *Mary Poppins?*"

"Yeah," But I hadn't seen the movie in quite a while.

The Lord asked, "What was he doing?"

"He was up on the ceiling laughing," I said.

"Do you know that there is an even more real realm than this one?" He said.

My first thought was, *how?*

"What happened when people came into his presence?" God asked.

As I thought about it, I realized that they were lifted. They began laughing. Children were even on the ceiling laughing uncontrollably. People tried to pull the kids down, but they couldn't control them. They were teaching the adults how to be kids. Finally, the kids said, "No, I want to go up. I want to go up."

As they went up, they did flips and somersaults. They began doing amazing things! It's because they were children.

God asked me, "But what was the uncle doing?"

"He was doing flips in the air, and so were the kids," I responded. It was impossible to separate the adults from the kids. Everybody looked the same. You couldn't tell who the adults were and who the kids were. They all were spinning and having fun. It was a perfect picture of joy. They were all laughing.

God said, "That realm can be more real than this one."

I wanted to know how.

He asked, "What did they have to do to come down?"

I thought for a minute then replied, "Well, they had to think about something sad, like when a dog died."

As they thought about things that saddened them, they began to come down from the ceiling.

My point is your circumstances don't need to dictate where you live. Thank you, Jesus! What would our world look like if we constantly walked

---

[45] Mary Poppins (1964) - IMDb

around with huge smiles? It would look like the music video in Mary Poppins, *"I Love to Laugh."* We will become like children, all looking the same. Think about it, what would the world look like if we all started walking around full of joy with huge smiles? Maybe our world would look like the uncle from "*Mary Poppins.*"

In the movie, people came into his presence thinking, this world is the worst it's ever been. But they walked into the uncle's house, and he was having a great time up on the ceiling, laughing just like a little kid. Mary Poppins tried to hold the children down, but they wanted to stay up in the atmosphere of joy. The atmosphere of joy changed the usual sad or annoyed atmosphere so much that even the table, an inanimate object, went up into the air.

When Mary Poppins said, "It's time to go."

The uncle started crying and said, "That is so sad. They always come, but they never stay."

The Holy Spirit was speaking to me about this. People love to get filled with joy and be in His presence. They think that laughter and joy can only be fleeting and last for a moment. They don't realize that God wants joy to be their daily lifestyle. Did you know that laughter is God's medicine for your body, soul, and mind? That revelation from the Holy Spirit changed my life, and it also changed my family's life for the best. God wants me to laugh every day.

The uncle changed the atmosphere with his laughter. We, too, can change the atmosphere of our lives and the lives of those around us by laughing. We can release joy into the atmosphere of our problems, and we can watch God work on all our problems. This may not seem to be effective if all you're used to is war.

I'm reminded of David and his son Solomon. David was a man who had dealt with war and conflict. His son, however, was a man of peace. I believe there is a time for war, but there is also a time for peace. This may also seem ineffective but let me assure you that it is highly effective.

Ecclesiastes 3:1-8 *NIV* says:

"There is a time for everything, and a season for every activity under the heavens: a time to be born and a time to die, a time to plant and a time to uproot, a time to kill and a time to heal, a time to tear down and a time to build, a time to weep and a time to laugh, a time to mourn and a time to dance, a time to scatter stones and a time to gather them, a time to embrace and a time to refrain from embracing, a time to search and a time to give up, a time to keep and a time to throw away, a time to tear and a time to mend, a time to be silent and a time to speak, a time to love and a time to hate, a time for war and a time for peace."

We can be going through all kinds of turmoil and strife, but if we keep our eyes focused on Jesus, He will make ways where there seems to be none. Most things in the Kingdom of God seem to be the exact opposite of what we tend to believe as worldly truth. The things that we perceive as worldly truth are most often lies, and the things that people see as lies about God are, in fact, the ultimate truth.

Laughter is an immensely powerful weapon that we don't use often enough. We should be using it every day. 2 Corinthians 10:4 *NIV* says, *"…the weapons we fight with are not the weapons of the world. On the contrary, they have divine power to demolish strongholds."* With every single breath of laughter, we are pulling down strongholds. When we laugh, we let the enemy know that his attacks against us do not move us because we know that God, our good Father has our backs, and He is always watching over us.

The next time the enemy comes to steal, kill, and destroy something in your life, I challenge you to permit yourself to laugh at whatever hardship you're facing. Even if it seems ridiculous to laugh, just go ahead and let yourself laugh. When we allow ourselves to laugh, we are filled with joy rather than the pain and sorrow of the moment. Remember that our Father up in heaven laughs at the plans of the enemy all the time. It is time we do the same thing.

In *Mary Poppins*, the people who were laughing looked like a pack of laughing hyenas.

What would it be like for us if we walk into a store and there is craziness going on, and people are getting upset? But then, we start laughing, and everything changes. I can tell you what it looks like because I have testimony after testimony about laughter. I have walked into many places with others, and we just started laughing and changing the atmosphere. So, you can do that too.

People might look at us like we are crazy, but others would eventually join in and laugh with us. Laughter changes the atmosphere no matter where you are. Did you know that people who don't even like joy will start to experience joy if they see you experiencing joy? Why? Because laughter is contagious.

People think they are only supposed to experience joy for a few fleeting moments. They don't realize that God wants laughter and joy to be a lifestyle for every one of us. He wants joy to be our lifestyle. We can live full of joy at any time, no matter what. I've been cultivating this vital truth in my own life for over ten years. I want to share it with others so they, too, can experience the fullness of joy in God's presence. Joy is a powerful tool against the darkness of this world. We wrestle every day with spiritual warfare. Joy is a tool we can use to combat our spiritual warfare. Laughter is and can be spiritual warfare, medicine, and strength.

As we learned earlier, joy is contagious. All it takes is one person to say, "I choose joy today." Try it for yourself. Don't take my word for it. You can ask the Holy Spirit, "Does this work?" And just get filled up with joy! Suddenly, as you walk by someone and are so full of joy, the person you passed next to just starts laughing. They don't even know why they are so happy. They just like being around you because you are so full of joy.

Now, everyone is drawn to you because your joy is contagious. We want joy, and it spreads to other people. It's not like you have to be fasting or doing something spiritual to hear from God. All I was doing was making breakfast for my family, and I got some profound truths from God.

As I was still thinking about this, I heard a pastor speaking a few weeks later. What subject did he bring up in his sermon? None other than Mary Poppins and the song "*I Love to Laugh.*" As soon as I heard him mention Mary Poppins, I started cracking up laughing with the revelation. So, I knew then that God was trying to get my attention and He was talking to me.

Laughter brings us up, while fear and worry bring us down. So, what would happen in our lives if we spent more time laughing than crying, and smiling rather than frowning? Joy would become an automatic part of our lives.

It is a sacrifice of praise when we do something we don't want to do. So, if you find that laughing is sacrificial praise, then put it on the altar before the King and spend time making that sacrifice to Him. The beauty of those sacrifices is that God always shows up during and through sacrifices in ways we never even thought possible.

Another interesting point that God pressed upon my heart is that I like to run. I like the feeling when I run, but I have to get in the right frame of mind to do it. There are days, weeks, and months when I don't run. But then I realized that when I do run, I feel better. My body will, at times, fight itself, and my body will say, "I don't want to run today."

But I have to remind myself of the physical, emotional, and even mental benefits running brings me. I can't just lie in bed and think about running to get results. I must get out of my bed, put on running shoes, and start running down my street. It takes work and commitment. I must get up and go if I want to see results happening in me and through me.

God gave each of us a body. We must figure out how to use it best physically, mentally, and emotionally every day.

The same is true with laughing. So many Christians think they can laugh only when it's appropriate or when they've heard a funny joke or watched a funny movie. That is a lie from the enemy. The notion binds many Christians, "I'll laugh only when I feel like it." Whenever I run, I can tell you that I falter most of the time. Nevertheless, I push through my laziness, and something extraordinary happens. I start to remind myself why I like to run and all the benefits it brings me.

If anyone reading this book feels like they need to have a reason to do something, realize that when you laugh, you are using one of the most powerful arsenals against the enemy. He has no sense of why you're laughing. It brings him confusion and dismay. He doesn't understand the joy you possess because he is not used to people using it on him. The best part is that when we laugh, we are simply saying, "God, we trust You despite what we don't see, hear, think, or feel. Our eyes are upon You to bring us through."

This positioning of our hearts makes the Holy Spirit happy.

Did you know there is a study by the University of Kentucky College of Agriculture, Food and Environment that says:

> *"The average adult laughs 17 times a day while a child laughs 300 times a day. There is a reason why we have always heard that laughter is the best medicine. Both humor and laughter can be effective self-care tools to help us cope with stress, especially in the workplace. Finding humor and laughter in stressful situations can give us a sense of perspective on our problems. And it's good for our health."[46]*

Kids may know something. Kids are often punished for laughing when they see someone else laughing. They, in turn, start laughing with each other, and then they can't stop.

As stated at the beginning of this chapter, laughter is contagious. So, if you want more fun and more friends in your life, just start laughing and see how many more authentic, genuine people you attract in your life. Watch how people start to want to be around you as you embrace this new truth of how real God is, and how real He can continue to be in your life. He wants to use His supernatural joy to rock your world in more ways than you can fathom, think of, or imagine. He said, "to multiply," which means being fruitful in every area of your life. He made this earth a place

---

[46]Bias Strips (uky.edu)

for us to be happy all the time. We must make a choice every single day to be happy.

There have been tests about laughter done on subways where one person laughs, and everyone else seems annoyed at first. Then soon, everyone starts laughing with one another, but earlier no one was talking to one another. It starts as a chuckle from one person, and it explodes into a full laughing fit until the subway stops and someone new gets on the subway. Then everyone else goes back to their normal routines until someone else starts laughing again. The more you're around people that laugh. The more people will want to be around you.

I want to share a testimony from an experience I had while ministering in Arizona. We were laughing over people as we prayed for them. That's the truth.

"Well, that's heresy," you might say.

No, it is Christ in you, the hope of glory.

As a result, Jesus lives inside of you, and the Word says in Joshua 1:3, *"Every place that the sole of your foot will tread upon I have given you, as I said to Moses." NKJV*

Here we are praying for people and just laughing and having fun. The Word says, *"unless you are converted and become as little children, you will by no means enter the kingdom of heaven." Matthew 18:3 NKJV*

What better way to do that than to come full of joy? So, we started laughing because there were some very ill people in the room. I asked them to raise their hands whenever they felt God touching them or when they were completely healed.

When one man raised his hand, I asked, "What is going on?"

He replied, "Nothing."

I said, "Oh, I guess you didn't understand. All I want is for people to raise their hands if they have been healed. We will laugh over you again."

As a result, people laughed over him, and I repeated the same thing. "When you are healed, raise your hand."

Sure enough, he raised his hand again, and I asked, "What happened?"

He replied, "Nothing."

I replied, "Oh, I don't think you're understanding, I want you to raise your hand when you're healed."

He said, "No, you don't understand."

"Really?" I asked.

"You don't understand. I have been hearing voices since I was four years old," he said.

Within five minutes, he was free of schizophrenia for the first time in twenty years. Schizophrenia was forced to leave! Do you know why? The enemy's greatest foe is joy. Do you remember what I said?

The joy of the Lord is your strength!

In other words, if the enemy can steal your joy, he gets your strength! It's obvious he doesn't want you to know this. His goal is to keep you in the dark. Because when you know who your Daddy is, then you know how good He is, and He is a good Daddy. He gives good gifts to His children. He never comes to kill, steal, or destroy. He comes to bring life and life abundantly.

I want to share one of my favorite scriptures. In Psalm 91, it says:

"He who dwells in the secret place of the Most High Shall abide under the shadow of the Almighty. I will say of the Lord, "He is my refuge and my fortress; My God, in Him I will trust..."NKJV

If you trust in Him, then trust in His Word. His Word says, "laughter is good medicine." Remember that God is sitting in the heavens and laughing, because of that we have permission, and we don't have to be afraid. We can live in joy; we can live in this realm every day. Remember Mary Poppins? Remember when God showed me that it doesn't matter your circumstances; that doesn't dictate where you live? You can live in this joy realm all the time. Just take in His truth, take in His promises; they are for *you,* and they are *true.*

Psalm 91 continues:

..."nor of the pestilences that walk in the darkness nor of the destruction that lays waste at noonday, a thousand may fall at your side, ten thousand at your right hand, but it shall not come near you only with your eyes will you look and see the reward of the wicked." and then it says, 'Because you have made the Lord who is my refuge even the most high, your dwelling place no evil, can come near you nor any plague shall come near your dwelling for He shall give His angels charge over you." That is good news! NKJV

Just like the parable in Matthew 25 where Jesus talks about the man with the talents, you can also use this passage regarding the gifts God gave you. Look at the gifts God gave you and figure out how you can use them to the best of your ability. Think about how you can share your talents and gifts that God has given you with others and how you can use them to bless them and bring Him glory. So many times, God gives us different talents, and we bury them. We say, "No, I'm going to keep these things to myself."

Sometimes we aren't even sure what to do with our talents or how to handle them in the best way possible. So, we just bury them deep down and forget about them as the business of our daily lives continues. But to the person who invested the talents in the bank, God seemed to say, "At least you did something worthwhile with the talents I gave you."

We must ask ourselves; do we really know what our talents are from God? Do we invest time in them? The person with the five talents also invested them in the bank and got a return on his investment. He got double what he had invested in the first place.

Like I said at the beginning of the book, God has a plan for you if God woke you up this morning. Trust His plan for your life today.

Godly Lifestyle Activation

God has given everyone the gift of laughter. It is our choice whether we steward it. Laughter can be a tool we can *use* to live a truly joyful life.

God's Truth

➢ The name Isaac means "he laughs."

"And Abraham called the name of his son who was born to him— whom Sarah bore to him—Isaac... And Sarah said, 'God has made me laugh, and all who hear will laugh with me.'" - Genesis 21:36 NKJV

➢ Because God knows the ending of the story, He laughs at the plans of the enemy. Likewise, we can laugh at the evil plans of the enemy.

"The righteous also shall see and fear and shall laugh at him, saying, 'Here is the man who did not make God his strength.'" - Psalm 52:67 NKJV

➢ Isaac knew he was a royal son because he knew his identity. When we know who we are and when we know our name, we can stand in God's strength and confidence. Knowing what we have in Christ, our laughter becomes spiritual warfare and destroys the enemy's plans.

"The Lord laughs at him. For He sees that his day is coming."- Psalm 37:13 NKJV

"But You, O Lord, shall laugh at them; You shall have all the nations in derision."- Psalm 59:8 NKJV

"I also will laugh at your calamity. I will mock when your terror comes." - Proverbs 1:26 NKJV

➤ God wants to use you to heal others, but He wants to heal you first. Then, He wants to fill you with joy so that you can go out and give it away.

"And God is able to make all grace abound toward you, that you, always having all sufficiency in all things, may have an abundance for every good work." - 2 Corinthians 9:8 NKJV

➤ You can't give away anything you don't already have.

"...that in a great trial of affliction the abundance of their joy and their deep poverty abounded in the riches of their liberality." - 2 Corinthians 8:2 NKJV

➤ God wants you to bring healing and restoration to others through joy and laughter.

"Now then, we are ambassadors for Christ, as though God were pleading through us: we implore you on Christ's behalf, be reconciled to God." - 2 Corinthians 5:20 NKJV

Your Response to God's Truth

Get together with a laughing partner, and each of you create a list of the obstacles you're facing in your current circumstance.

Give your list to your partner and spend some time laughing over each other's problems.

Once you are finished, ask for your list back and rip it up.

Scriptures for Further Study

"Every place that the sole of your foot will tread upon I have given you, as I said to Moses." - Joshua 1:3 NKJV

Then he said to them, "Go your way, eat the fat, drink the sweet, and send portions to those for whom nothing is prepared; for this day is holy to our Lord. Do not sorrow, for the joy of the Lord is your strength." – Nehemiah 8:10 NKJV

"I also will laugh at your calamity; I will mock when your terror comes" -
Proverbs 1:26 NKJV

"and said, "Assuredly, I say to you, unless you are converted and become as little children, you will by no means enter the kingdom of heaven."
- Matthew 18:3 NKJV

"...that in a great trial of affliction the abundance of their joy and their deep poverty abounded in the riches of their liberality." - 2 Corinthians 8:2
NKJV

CHAPTER SEVEN

Laughter Brings Connection

There are many things in this life that connect us to one another. Food, babies, church, the beach, the mountains, concerts, music, art, social media, etc. But there is one thing that is universal and connects us all and that is laughter. Laughter is something that usually comes natural to children as well as adults. We all laugh but usually, we don't know why we laughed. We feel this emotion well up inside that we can't contain, and it comes out as laughter. Even a newborn baby at times will laugh and no one told it a joke or tickled it. We laugh and no one even taught us to laugh. Laughing is natural to humans.

Psalm 126 *NKJV* says, *"When the Lord brought back the captivity of Zion, we were like those who dream. Then our mouth was filled with laughter."* God will fill your mouth with laughter at different times in your life. It's a promise from His word. It is biblical to laugh, and I will share key elements that will radically change your life. I pray that your life will never be the same if you take all these keys and start adding them to your life.

Laura Kurtz, a social psychologist from the University of North Carolina, did a study about couples and their ability to laugh with one another.

> *"We can all think of a time when we were laughing, and the person next to us just sat there totally silent," she says. "All of a sudden that one moment takes a nosedive. We wonder why the other person isn't laughing, what's wrong with*

them, or maybe what's wrong with us, and what
might that mean for our relationship. In general,
couples who laugh more together tend to have
higher-quality relationships," she says. "We can
refer to shared laughter as an indicator of greater
relationship quality."[47]

Jesus died on the cross and gave us an inheritance, and He gave us keys. One of the keys is joy. Joy is enormously powerful! This experience is in the kingdom of God, and it is a bummer that we have, for the most part, kicked joy out of the church. But you know what? The world hasn't kicked joy out. The world is crying out for joy, and they have tried to mimic joy because the enemy is always a counterfeiter of what God has for the Church. So, we can be happy to be alive! How many of you can say you are glad to be alive? Do you live like that every day?

When we are full of joy, things in our lives change and, in the people, to which we are connected. Laughter connects groups of people and brings intimacy and transparency. Let me share an example.

I went to South Korea a while back and taught teenagers to laugh. Instead of laughing with all their hearts, they just kept covering their mouths to cover their teeth. I told them to put their hands down and not cover their mouths. I told them to laugh with everything they had within them. When someone hears you laughing, it brings intimacy.

Another example is when you and your spouse are in the middle of an argument, and then your spouse starts laughing. Even if you are mad at them for laughing, you can't help but laugh. Then you get mad at yourself. You say in your head thinking, "What are you doing? I'm mad at you! You shouldn't be making me laugh. You can't be telling me this stupid joke right now!"

Laughter also helps us maturely manage conflicts. If you're not fighting with your spouse or loved ones, you will have a deeper relationship.

---

[47] Shared Laughter In a Relationship Indicates a Happier Couple | Time

When you're laughing with other people, you won't be depressed. If my husband and I start feeling weighed down, the first thing he says is, "Come on. We need to laugh together."

Just like when "iron sharpens iron" - Proverbs 27:17 *NKJV*, when you laugh with someone, you're sharpening another person. You're helping another person to be happy.

"Shared laughter says that they see the world in the same way, and it momentarily boosts their sense of connection. Perceived similarities end up being an important part of the story of relationships," says social psychologist Sara Algoe.[48] She is the co-founder of the study by Laura Kurtz, mentioned earlier in this chapter.

In the study of humor research by psychiatrist Joseph Richman, M.D., a professor emeritus at Albert Einstein Medical Center in Bronx, New York, says, *"In addition to its biological effects, laughter may also improve our mood by social means. Telling a joke, particularly one that illustrates a shared experience or problem, increases our sense of belonging and social cohesion,"*.[49] He believes that laughter psychologically connects us to others, and laughter counteracts feelings of alienation, a significant factor in depression and suicide.

Laughter is very important. I hope that you can see that studies and personal experience show that laughter brings us together. It connects us as well as heals the body and mind. In a study of depressed and suicidal senior citizens, the patients who recovered were the ones with a sense of humor, reported psychiatrist Joseph Richman, M.D., professor emeritus at Albert Einstein Medical Center in Bronx, New York.[50]

All of this makes sense considering laughter's numerous psychological effects. *"After you laugh, you go into a more relaxed state,"* explains John Morreall, Ph.D., president of HUMORWORKS Seminars in Tampa, Florida. *"Your blood pressure and heart rate drop below normal levels, so you feel profoundly relaxed."*[51]

---

[48] How Laughter Brings Us Together (berkeley.edu)
[49] Putting Laughter in Context: Shared Laughter as Behavioral Indicator of Relationship Well-Being - PMC (nih.gov)
[50] Happily Ever Laughter | Psychology Today
[51] Happily Ever Laughter | Psychology Today

Some of laughter's other psychological effects are less obvious. *"For one thing, it helps us think more creatively,"* says Morreall. *"It encourages an out-of-the-body way of looking at things."*[52]

Laughing can be done in just about any location. Laughing in the workplace is becoming more and more uncommon these days. People think they're only supposed to be serious at work and never allowed to let go and have fun. But this cannot be further from the truth.

> *"Laughter Links is a program teaching non-humor-dependent yoga-based, purposeful aerobic laughter in a group setting. It is based upon the work of Dr. Madan Kataria, a cardiologist in Mumbai, India. He combined medical research and modern science to create his own laughter technique."*[53]

Workplace laughter groups used this laughing technique and met for fifteen consecutive workdays. "A professional laughter coach who had direct training in Dr. Kataria's approach led the classes. The program began with a forty-five-minute orientation session covering the background and rationale for the intervention."[50]

In the orientation session, the following was emphasized:

➤ Humor can be very subjective because of everyone's tastes, values, languages, and cultures, so some humor can be offensive.

➤ Alternatively, laughter is an instinctive behavior rooted in our biological beings. Therefore, it is acceptable and accessible to everyone.

➤ It is important to foster laughter in an atmosphere of respect for others.

➤ Laughter creates an aerobic effect like that of moderate exercise.

---

[52] Happily Ever Laughter | Psychology Today
[53] Effect of Workplace Laughter Groups on Personal Efficacy Beliefs | Heidi Beckman; Nathan Regier; Judy Young | download (booksc.me)

"For the next 14 days, participants spent 15 minutes before work or during their lunch break engaging in purposeful laughter. Each class began with participants practicing the basic yoga-based laughter stance and gentle stretching. Participants then engaged in guided exercises to practice abdominal laughter. The basic exercise started with a vocalization of "ho-ho-ho, ha-ha-ha, he-he-he, and then proceeded with hearty unbounded laughter. More advanced exercises blended laughter with a variety of activities such as shaking hands, looking each other in the eye, or playing interactive games. At no point was humor used to facilitate the laughter."[54]

I share Dr. Kataria's approach or strategy with you because he is using a God principle of laughter and he is getting some results even though he is not really founded on Christianity as a personal discipline. This shows that the principles of God will work for anyone because they are universal.

Some participants of the study found humor in some aspects of the class. "At times, the challenge of laughing on cue became the trigger for involuntary laughter."[55] Overall, the four hypotheses of this study were supported. An increase in self-regulation, optimism, positive emotion, and social identification was significant and maintained at a 90-day follow-up.

That daily fifteen-minute intervention could produce such significant positive changes in the key areas of self-efficiency, without changing any other environmental factors, is encouraging to the field of occupational health..."[56]

Laughter is powerful. It's so good for our souls. In addition, laughter can help you excel in your place of employment. It has been shown to relieve levels of stress at work. The above research I've mentioned shows

---

[54]Effect of Workplace Laughter Groups on Personal Efficacy Beliefs | Heidi Beckman; Nathan Regier; Judy Young | download (booksc.me)

[55]Effect of Workplace Laughter Groups on Personal Efficacy Beliefs | Heidi Beckman; Nathan Regier; Judy Young | download (booksc.me)

[56]Effect of Workplace Laughter Groups on Personal Efficacy Beliefs | Heidi Beckman; Nathan Regier; Judy Young | download (booksc.me)

that if employers allow their employees time to laugh, it will improve their health. So, if you have a business and want your employees to stay healthy, start setting aside ten minutes a day to laugh with your employees. Then, watch the productivity of your office go up drastically and improve. The productivity of your office will improve because all your employees will be and can be happy to come to work every day. Everyone in your office will have good endorphins rushing through their bodies. Laughter changes the atmosphere, and it also relieves stress that is so common in the workplace.

Just like so many people use LOL (laugh out loud) in texts and emails, we should actually do that. You might think, *I can laugh quietly to myself.* But trust me when you laugh out loud it affects your whole being. There's something about it when you hear yourself laughing. It has a profound effect on you.

They say when you are speaking, being able to hear yourself is profound. Even when you read scriptures, it is food to hear what is being told to you by God. It is good to read the scriptures out loud. When you laugh, you're making it very clear to yourself and everyone around you that whatever comes to try and hinder you has no power over you in the name of God. You are saying, I have Jesus in me, and He is more powerful, and I'm going to laugh right now. I don't care what the situation is, and I don't care how I feel because God is bigger.

Why would we not want joy in our hearts and fill our hearts with laughter? We need to release the joy He gives us. I'm telling you right now to start laughing for even thirty seconds. Then go up to laughing for one minute, then two, then three, then ten minutes per day. You will feel stronger and healthier whenever you laugh instead of stressed out.

So, in the name of Jesus, I release joy over you and your life. The benefits of laughter in your life are so profound. The benefits are going to far outweigh any conversation you might have where people might say, this is kind of ridiculous. You will feel stronger and be laughing all the way to the bank, and you won't be spending all your money on medicine. You're going straight to the author. You're going straight to the word of

God, where God is constantly able to tell you that He has an antidote to your problems. That antidote is laughter. It can be better in some cases than any medicine you could take.

There is a scare going on with Covid-19 being rampant in our world. They have given us vaccines and boosters, but they may not figure out the exact cure for it. They told us that the vaccines would make it harder to get Covid-19, and everyone wanted them, and some are still waiting to get them. Everyone under the sun wants the boosters and the vaccines because they think the vaccine will protect them. We can have that same hunger and thirst for God's Word and the beautiful things He tells us.

Imagine if we had that same hunger and thirst for the Lord that the world had for getting the Covid-19 vaccines. Imagine how much God could continue to work on our lives if we tell people that God is the proper antidote for everything we're dealing with as individuals, society, and nation.

God has given us the ultimate serum of laughter and it's inside of you already, and the good news is that it's free. You know that fear is the exact opposite of love, right? Sadness and depression are also the opposite of joy and laughter. We should be so happy every day that we don't have to work hard to find joy in our everyday life. We can ask God to help us find joy in our circumstances.

I invite you to have a healthy dose of laughter right here. Just let yourself go. Let yourself laugh, even when you don't feel like it. Grab your mate, your children, or whomever you can find and begin to laugh. Allow yourself to have a hefty dose of laughter every day. Laughter is the best medicine, and the best Man gave it to us as a gift. His name is Jesus. In the same way that He gives us free salvation, He allows us to experience His peace, love, joy, grace, mercy, and laughter daily. We can ask Him to fill our bodies, lives, and minds with laughter, and we must laugh even when it's the last thing we want to do.

I also want to ask, if you haven't asked Jesus into your heart, when are you going to ask Him into your heart? Ask Him into your life and your heart. If you have never experienced that kind of joy, I invite you to ask for His laughter and joy to come into your life right now.

All you have to say is, "Jesus, I want you in my life. I ask that You come into my life and make Your home inside me. I ask that You forgive me of my sins, and I embrace You and the joy You freely give me."

Every time you pray, I pray that you will be so filled with God's presence because His presence is so full of joy.

Godly Lifestyle Activation

One of the greatest joys that a person can ever have is receiving Jesus as their personal Savior. He alone is the source of all true joy and laughter. Everything else pales in comparison to the joy that comes from having a personal relationship with Jesus.

God's Truth:

➢ God wants you to help people rebuild the broken-down walls of laughter in their lives. you can do this as you rebuild your own walls. Nehemiah had a king who was able to provide resources for the reconstruction of his walled city. So likewise, we have a King who desires a complete restoration of our lives. The story of the rebuilding of the wall is in Nehemiah 2. *Then the king said to me, "What do you request? And the king granted them to me according to the good hand of my God upon me."* The Spirit of God is upon us to raise walls that are broken.

"And they shall rebuild the old ruins, they shall raise up the former desolations, and they shall repair the ruined cities, The desolations of many generations." - Isaiah 61:4 NKJV

➢ God gave Nehemiah the wisdom to have every family build their own section of the wall. That is the way we start, by building our own segments of the wall. Your segment on the wall of your life that is broken down is joy and laughter. God needs that joy and laughter back in your life to bring healing to the body, spirit, and soul.

➢ The process of laughter and joy in your life begins when you become so full of joy that it overflows into other people's lives. It is God who brings life and good gifts to His children.

"We laughed and laughed and overflowed with gladness. We were left shouting for joy and singing your praise. All the nations saw it and joined in, saying, "The Lord has done great miracles for them!"." -Psalm 126:2 TPT

➤ You can have a continual feast if you keep the joy in your heart.

"But he who is of a merry heart has a continual feast."- Proverbs 15:15 NKJV

Your Response to God's Truth

Think of ways to bring intimacy between you and another person through laughter. What can you laugh about?

Find a friend or loved one to do things together this week to make each other laugh.

This week try to laugh each time someone tries to upset you.

In what ways can you make your spouse or loved one laugh?

Scriptures for Further Study

"A merry heart does good, like medicine, but a broken spirit dries the bones." - Proverbs 17:2 2 NKJV

"Let your fountain be blessed and rejoice with the wife of your youth. As a loving deer and a graceful doe, let her breasts satisfy you at all times; And always be enraptured with her love." - Proverbs 5:18-19 NKJV

"For it is better, if it is the will of God, to suffer for doing good than for doing evil."- 1 Peter 3:17-20 NKJV

"For the flesh lusts against the Spirit, and the Spirit against the flesh; and these are contrary to one another so that you do not do the things that you wish." - Galatians 5:17 NKJV

"As iron sharpens iron, so a man sharpens the countenance of his friend." - Proverbs 27:17 NKJV

"So, he answered and said, 'You shall love the Lord your God with all your heart, with all your soul, with all your strength, and with all your mind, and your neighbor as yourself.'" - Luke 10:27 NKJV

The Laughter Test

I took a road trip to Washington to see friends and family with a friend, my son, and his friend for the weekend before going on a ministry trip to the Midwest. The night before our journey back to California, we all decided to stay with my friend's family since it was on the way home. I slept in the room where their baby slept. They put me in there since the baby always sleeps through the night. Well, this night, the baby did not sleep. She cried most of the night, so I did not get a good night's sleep. We woke up early the next day to head home. My friend had decided she would drive the first part of our trip since I had not slept well. While she was driving, I would sleep and then be ready to take over the rest of the way home. That was our plan.

I decided the best way to get some good sound sleep was to use an eye mask and my earplugs to help block light and sound since the rest of the crew was up talking and listening to music. The trip started without any problems; everything changed about an hour into the trip.

We hit a patch of ice and started spinning out of control. Suddenly, I was jolted awake when I heard my son's voice let out a blood-curdling scream from the backseat. Then before I could even remove my eye mask, I lifted my hand and started praying very loudly in tongues. By the time I ripped off the eye mask all I could see were the headlights of a semi-truck headed straight for us. My friend started saying, "Jesus take the wheel," over and over again.

Suddenly the most amazing but frighting thing happened. It was as though our car was dancing across the busy freeway as we were spinning. We missed every car, including the semi-truck, and we landed hyper-extended over a ditch on the other side of the road. We landed in the only area we could have without all of us being killed. Obviously, it shook all of us up. Then if our ordeal was not bad enough, we ended up watching several more cars start to spin out of control. We also witnessed the police officer who stopped to help us almost get hit by a car. We were sitting in the car with a front-row seat to all the action. We continued to pray and believe that no one would be injured. When all vehicles came to a stop, we were so thankful; no one else was injured and no cars crashed. Once we got our car back on the road, I decided that I would drive the rest of the way.

This trip which should have taken a little over eleven hours turned into a grueling seventeen-hour journey. My nerves were shot, and I was exhausted, but the mother bear in me came out and I was determined that all of us would get home safely no matter what it took!

My friend and I had a ministry trip scheduled, so about three hours after arriving home; we were on a plane to Oklahoma. When I first got there, I felt fine, and we ministered for a few days. Then we went to another city to minister at another church. That is when I started noticing something was off with my body. I felt dizzy and not well. I shrugged it off and thought my symptoms were due to getting words of knowledge for some of their church members. I also called my mom to ask her to pray for me. She suggested that perhaps I lacked protein so, I ate some peanut butter and felt better. Then, the day we headed to the airport to fly home; things started to worsen. I got to the airport and felt like I was going to pass out and was having a difficult time breathing, so again I ate some peanut butter and a banana, thinking that would fix the problem.

Well, that is when the first panic attack set in; however, because I had never had one before, I did not know what I was experiencing. I was afraid of passing out, so I just kept moving. Little did I know that when you feel like you're going to pass out the best thing to do is lay down and put your feet up. I was doing the total opposite which was causing me to have even more problems.

Eventually, the airport staff called 911 and I was taken out of the airport on a gurney to the ambulance. Once I got in the ambulance, I started to feel a little better so I started thinking maybe I could still make my flight home. As I was trying to decide, the EMT told me that if they didn't take me now, I may not make it. With that as a possibility, I decided I better go to the hospital.

After many hours and many tests, I was released. Unfortunately, a few hours later, when I returned to the hotel, I started to have the same symptoms; I felt like I couldn't breathe and had chest pain. The ambulance was called again. They checked me out and said they could take me, but it might not be wise if they didn't find anything the first time. I agreed, and they left. I just tried to focus on something else to make it through the night and ensure I was on the plane first thing in the morning. I felt if I could get home, things would be better.

Until this point, I had seen a doctor five times in the ten years leading up to this incident. I got home and thought, okay, I am home and can rest, but about twelve hours later, I started feeling dizzy and off-balance again and headed to the hospital. Little did I know that that was the beginning of what I would consider a nightmare and a fight for my life. I would call my mom, telling her that I couldn't relax every night when it was time to go to bed. I was doing everything I could to relax by praying and speaking life over myself. But even with doing that and asking God to heal me from this anxiety, I would still wake up at 3 a.m. with full-blown panic attacks. I ended up having nine ambulance rides and seventeen emergency room visits over the next six weeks.

Remember I said I had been to the doctor four or five times in the last ten years, so this was not normal for me. Every time I would go to the hospital, the doctors would tell me that it was just anxiety and stress. They would promptly send me back home, only to see me again in a few days. On my fourth visit, they ran a test to rule out a heart attack. Since they had just lost another woman at the hospital that day, they wanted to make sure they weren't missing anything else. That is when they told me my body was starting to shut down. They also asked if I drank a lot since my liver was not looking good. I started to chuckle since I hardly even had a glass of wine. They also told me I needed to see a cardiologist since when I did the test, my blood pressure dropped to eighty, which is not good. I had been diagnosed with an elevated thyroid, postural hypotension, low blood pressure, and gastritis. In addition, my liver enzymes were a little high. Unfortunately, all those things overcame me at once, which caused the perfect storm to happen in my body. I went from being healthy one minute to being on over twenty medications with horrible side effects the next.

I went to the cardiologist and said, "Okay, what pill do I need to take to get well?" Usually, any time I went to the doctor, they gave me a pill, and a few days later, I felt fine again. He said that I would not be able to drive and that I needed to limit my energy level. I was also told I should not drive until they knew I wouldn't have another episode, so my world was spinning out of control."

I felt so helpless and scared. I was put on a rigorous and restrictive diet where I could barely eat anything. Here I was at my lowest and my mom had driven down from Washington State to take care of me, then while I was at my doctor's appointment with her, she passed out. She was taken to the hospital via ambulance. So now I was worried about her and trying to deal with my health concerns. After a couple of days, my mom was well enough to help me out.

We went to the store to buy groceries for me to eat. As I was in the grocery store, I felt overwhelmed as I walked down each aisle, realizing all the things I could not eat. Since I didn't know how long this would last, I wasn't sure if I would ever be able to eat again. I decided to go to the car. I was so discouraged. Tears dripped down my face as I wondered why this was happening and what I could do. I noticed a message on my phone and listened to a voice message. It was a praise report from a lady I had prayed for the year prior. That previous year, *at the same exact store*, I had walked up to her and asked her if she had knee pain. She said she did, so we prayed and laughed over her knee, and it started to feel better. She shared that she had cancer, so I prayed with her again, and we laughed over cancer. Remember, I was not laughing at her. I was laughing with her for her breakthrough. Now, one year later, I was sitting in the parking lot where that all happened, feeling so defeated when I hear her testimony. She has been trying to get a hold of me for over six months. After our encounter the year before, she had moved to Jamaica and was not able to share that her cancer was in remission! Suddenly, my tears weren't ones of discouragement anymore. Tears of joy flooded my eyes as the realization of the goodness and mercy of God gave me the hope that I needed at that exact moment.

Unfortunately, I ended up getting sick to the point that I was bedridden for almost five months with minimal exercise since I had to conserve my energy to make sure my blood pressure did not drop dangerously low. After this continued for several months, I had a chance to stay with my mom to help me recover. I happened to have a friend in Washington who was not only a doctor but also a natural doctor. She helped me get off all the medication causing horrible side effects. She put me on more natural medicines to help my body heal. I am forever grateful that God used her to help me get well and save my life. After many more tests, I was diagnosed with an autoimmune thyroid condition called Hashimoto thyroiditis. This condition affects every organ in your body and your energy level. It is where your body starts attacking itself. That is why I was told on one of my many visits that my organs were shutting down. The condition affected everything around me too. For example, whenever the weather changes, which changes a lot in Washington state, my body would be at a level ten pain. To make matters worse, all the pain medication they gave me had horrible side effects, and it didn't even touch the pain. It also caused me to be nauseated all the time, which would start the whole cycle of anxiety all over again.

That is when I heard God tell me, "It's time to laugh." I thought I was hearing things, so I ignored it, but I kept hearing God say, "It is time to laugh." I told Him I was in excruciating pain and didn't feel like laughing.

He said, "I know; I want you to laugh anyway." This is where my laughter test began.

Remember, I had many people, very well known ministers, praying over me. When I was in the School of Ministry, people kept saying, "I speak joy over you." I didn't realize at the time that I was going to need that joy over my life and in my heart, for a battle, I would face years later. They all kept saying "more joy". To be honest, I got to the point where I was saying, "Can they pray something else over me besides joy?" Yes, let's just laugh over that, ha ha ha. I wished they would pray anything but joy over me. I felt I had been given enough joy, ha ha ha. Let's laugh at that too! Well, this is where all the prayers of laughter and joy were going to be put to the test. Literally, while I was bedridden, I began to try to laugh with tears dripping down my face in so much pain sometimes the only thing I could get out was a very faint ha ha. No emotion, just the ha ha ha. It was so much work to try and laugh.

It is easy to laugh when everything is going well. Usually, you see people laugh when they hear or see something funny, but this was different. There was nothing funny, there was only pain and a lot of it. I did not feel like laughing nor did I want to laugh. But I also know that when I hear the Lord's voice, I want to be obedient. I continued to let out very pathetic laughter sounds with many tears. I wish I could tell you I laughed once and I was better, but that was not the case. I had to purposefully make myself laugh. Do you know how hard it is to laugh when you are in pain? It is not easy, nor is it normal.

I started looking for ways to laugh. I realized the more I laughed, the better I felt. I would watch funny movies, call my friends, and ask other for help when I needed to laugh right then. So, they helped me and would laugh too, which made them feel better also. I would watch videos of laughing babies on YouTube and laugh, and then you would never believe what I watched on YouTube. Okay, ready? I watched laughing hyenas... ha ha ha. Yes! Remember the name I ran away from as a child? This creature that I thought was so ugly was what God was using to help heal me through their laughter. I would watch them, I would start to chuckle, and then. I would start to laugh. I began to get my joy back.

Because of all the sickness, I had racked up $50,000 in medical expenses from my emergency room visits. But I began to laugh and laugh over that debt and watched God take it down bit by bit. Laughing would cause me to start laughing more. I spent hours and hours watching funny shows. I did anything and everything to keep laughing. As I was lying in bed, God repeatedly reminded me how hearty laughter was good for my health. He would remind me every hour that it was time for me to laugh again.

After several months I started to feel better. I was still dealing with anxiety, but the rest of my body responded to the natural medicines I was taking and a whole lot of laughter. Also, I was beginning to eat again which slowly built up my strength and energy levels to where I could move back to California. Even when I got home, I continued to practice laughing whenever I could. There were times when I would be laughing for several hours, but I knew it was helping me to get well, so that made me want to do it more. It was genuinely becoming my new normal. Then one morning, I started to have another full-blown panic attack. I started praying, speaking life, laughing, anything to calm myself. That is when I received a revelation. It may sound morbid, but this was the revelation: *whether I live or die, I win!*

When I had been in a near-fatal car accident it must have triggered something in my body. Then, to add insult to injury, as I was in the back of an ambulance trying to decide if I should just get on my scheduled flight, I had been told if I didn't go with them, I might die. These are all things that triggered fear at a level I had never experienced before in my life, causing me to have very severe panic attacks. Now, God is giving me this revelation. Whether I live or die, I win. After hearing those words, I said, "That is it. I am exhausted, so I am going to lie back down and go to sleep. If I wake up in the morning, praise Jesus! If I don't, that just means I wake up in Heaven with Jesus!" Suddenly, the fear that had gripped me for so many months seemed to subside. I lay down and went to sleep. The following day I woke up fully charged and felt so much better.

Of course, if the enemy can't trip you up, he will try again, and sure enough, a few weeks later, another panic attack attempted to come. This time I laughed and said those exact words, *"whether I live or die, I win,"* and it went away. I have not had another panic attack like I used to get. I might get a small one that will try to come, but I know I have the tools to combat it now. I had to keep telling myself that a few more times because the enemy doesn't just quit when he doesn't get the desired results. He waits for a while then attacks again. However, because I had the key in the arsenal of truth in my heart about laughter, I could keep using it and winning over his attacks. So, I was able to withstand his attacks.

Since that revelation from God, I have never had another severe panic attack. God's mercy and grace continued to be with me as I healed daily. Finally, I was well enough to start driving and even started running about three miles a day which was a big deal! When this all started, I was not even able to walk five feet. God is so Good! Then a few months later, I was out ministering again, even taking a couple of long airplane trips to Brazil to minister. As of this writing, the only medicine that I still take is my thyroid medicine. Which reminds me, I need to make sure I am laughing before I take it, ha ha ha.

It has been eight years since I was that sick. Have I dealt with sickness since then? Yes, and guess what my default has become? You guessed it, ha ha ha. Even if I am in pain, it may take me a few hours, but the laughter eventually begins to happen because I know the power of laughter. I have seen it work in my life and in others too. Well, if you think there is only one test, ha ha ha, another came about a year ago.

I woke up early one morning to use the restroom, and on the way back to bed, I looked in the mirror and saw my face. One side of my face had dropped. Instead of going into all-out panic attack mode, I was calm about it. Yes, I was freaked out because I knew that could mean I could have a stroke, but even then, as I was calling 911, I didn't have a panic attack. I didn't know whether I was having a stroke or what was happening. When

I went to the emergency room, the doctors diagnosed me with Bell's palsy. Bell's palsy is a condition that causes sudden weakness in the muscles on one side of the face. In most cases, the weakness is temporary and significantly improves over weeks. The weakness makes half of the face appear to droop. Smiles are one-sided, and the eye on the affected side resists closing. Eventually, things got back to normal on my face, and life continued. It was a blessing that it happened during covid when everyone had to wear masks, so no one saw me! Ha ha ha. Then the same thing happened to me about six months after the first incident. This time my mouth was affected, but only one side of it was opening. It was crazy, and it was one of the weirdest experiences I've ever had in my entire life. It freaked me out a bit but at the same time, I felt God's peace surrounding me through both of those incidences. During these two times, I never had a panic attack.

Laughter is one tool that God uses. I want to be clear. God used the prayers of family and friends, my friend who was a natural doctor, and laughter to bring my healing. Laughter was one part of my healing and an important part. And it was a test. It is not easy to laugh when your body is screaming to do the opposite. I want you to know that even when you don't feel like you can, God will. He will meet you right there, even with tears dripping down your face. Even amid a scary uncontrollable situation. Even if you feel like I am making this up, trust me. I laughed through all of this. Suppose you laugh like taking medicine. What would happen if you took your medication and added laughter as part of your prescription? For example, if you take your treatment three times a day, start laughing three times a day, and watch what God does for you. Watch how your body responds. I pray you will receive a breakthrough just like I did.

Godly Lifestyle Activation

In the Bible it says laughter is good medicine this isn't just words but truth. God has given each of us a key to health and it happens when we open our mouth and start laughing. There are times we have to initiate our breakthrough then the Holy Spirit steps in and helps us.

"Then he broke through and transformed all my wailing into a whirling dance of ecstatic praise! He has torn the veil and lifted from me the sad heaviness of mourning. He wrapped me in the glory-garments of gladness."
- Psalm 30:11 (TPT)

God's Truth

> ➢ It is healthy for your body to laugh even when you don't feel like it or think you can't.

"A joyful, cheerful heart brings healing to both body and soul. But the one whose heart is crushed struggles with sickness and depression."
- Proverbs 17:22 (TPT)

> ➢ When we don't know what to say we can always call on Jesus

"Therefore God has highly exalted him and bestowed on him the name that is above every name, so that at the name of Jesus every knee should bow, in heaven and on earth and under the earth, and every tongue confess that Jesus Christ is Lord, to the glory of God the Father"
- Philippians 2:9–11 (ESV)

> ➢ Laughing is not just for good times but for the painful ones too

"A cheerful heart puts a smile on your face, but a broken heart leads to depression." - Proverbs 15:13 (TPT)

> ➢ When we laugh it can be a type of worship to our Heavenly Father especially when it is a sacrifice.

And now shall mine head be lifted up above mine enemies round about me: therefore, will I offer in his tabernacle sacrifices of joy; I will sing, yea, I will sing praises unto the LORD. to him. - Psalm 27:6 (NIV)

Your Response to God's Truth

This week if you take medication or vitamins laugh before you take them each day and pay attention to how you feel

Make a decision to choose laughter the next time you are in pain. The way you do this is by practicing before you need it. Every day just try to add a few ha ha ha's by watching something funny.

Pray for someone, maybe even yourself, that God would give you more joy.

Scriptures for Further Study:

"Blessed are you who hunger now, for you shall be filled. Blessed are you who weep now, for you shall laugh." - Luke 6:21 (NKJV)

"Then our mouth was filled with laughter and our tongue with joyful shouting..." - Psalm 126:2 (NASB)

"He will yet fill your mouth with laughter and your lips with joyful shouting..." Job 8:21 (AMP)

"For you will go out with joy and be led out with peace. The mountains and the hills will break forth into singing before you, and the trees of the field shall clap their hands." - Isaiah 55:12 (NKJV)

"Then young women will dance and be glad, young men and old as well. I will turn their mourning into gladness; I will give them comfort and joy instead of sorrow." - Jeremiah 31:13 (NIV)

Miracles Still Continue Today

God blesses us with gifts. When He does, He loves for us to use them for the kingdom of God. As I used the gift of laughter in my own life, God showed me that He wanted me to use it all the time, even when I didn't think it was time to use it. I will tell you a secret; God loves spontaneity.

God wants to talk to you, me, and the world more than we know. He is always wanting to love on us. Many times, when God talks to us, it looks quite different than we were expecting.

The laughter of the Lord is a wonderful gift that God wants to share with everyone, and you never know where that will occur. But wherever it happens, God will meet us right where we are. He wants us to keep the laughter going in our lives because you never know who needs deliverance.

But God also does miracles in very strange and profound ways. Laughter is one of those ways but there are many. He is forever the God of miracles. The miracles of the Bible have not ceased, and they are not the only miracles that God will perform. Great miracles are still happening even today. I want to show you in this chapter how God will do strange and unexpected miracles as you yield to being His vessel of goodness to hurting people.

While having fellowship one night with friends they mentioned that they were going to for a walk and asked if I wanted to join them. I thought, sure why not?

It was about 8:00 p.m. when we decided to go out and see what God wanted to do spontaneously on the street. We walked down the street by a gas station, saw a gentleman, and spoke to him.

"Hey, is your name Tim?"

The guy said, "No, my name is Joel." Immediately, I started thinking of Joel 2:22 and hearing different scriptures in my head and heart.

We continued to walk on down the street when it looked like we failed to get the right name. Then my friend said, "Oh man, I could tell you about a friend. He went through a whole week of having epic failure after epic failure. He was trying to get people's names, and he couldn't get anybody's names."

We were trying, and we were practicing hearing the voice of God. So, we started praying, and my friend said, "Holy Spirit, will you just give us words of knowledge for names?"

And then they shared a couple of names they got, and I said, "Well, I heard the name, Scott."

We kept walking, and in the meantime, several other guys come walking by.

I said, "Hey, is your name, Scott?"

And it became a running joke. They teased me, "Oh, Kristina, maybe this is Scott that is coming next."

As we got down to the Dollar Store, it was closed. We continued walking around. And we were just loving Jesus and sharing the testimony of Jesus with people.

My friend shared how his cousin just got saved that day; it was just incredible. It was just giving glory and honor to Jesus!

We started walking back and decided to stop at a liquor store. While we were in the liquor store, we were laughing, releasing God's presence, and praying. We prayed that every person who tried those drinks would have a Holy Spirit encounter.

Then we walked out of there after getting some water. We were walking back, and one of the guys said, "Hey, can we stop at this little convenience store?"

We agreed and walked in there, and guess what? A man was standing in there with his little nametag, and I looked at it, and I said, "Your name is Scott?" He said, "Yes."

I began to share with him how much God loved him, how God is chasing him down, how much he is known and just speaking life over him.

He was very thankful and said, "Thank you so much. Everything you said was so right on. And I know God is calling me; I know it."

He continued, "I hear Him all the time. I see different things He is doing."

So, I told Scott, "He is not finished with you. He loves you."

It was an incredible moment to hear God give us a name of a person and then run into that person and minister to them. God loves everyone so much and wants them to know it.

When you think about it, it is a miracle to minister to people when God tells you something about them. There are many such miracles in the Bible. Miracles are not gone. They are alive and well today just like in Bible times. God is still in the miracle-working business with His people and in the lives of those lost. Anyone can get a miracle. God does not pick and choose who will get one.

I want to increase your faith for miracles because God has one for you. Jesus went about doing miracle after miracle for people. Some of them He did for people, and they didn't even ask for a miracle. Let's look at some of them because the goodness and kindness of God were present to heal. You will see from these miracles that Jesus was full of compassion for people and loved them despite themselves. He is still in the business of doing miracles today and He will do one for you.

Miracles of Jesus

Jesus Changes Water into Wine: John 2:1-11 *(NKJV)*

On the third day there was a wedding in Cana of Galilee, and the mother of Jesus was there. Now both Jesus and His disciples were invited to the wedding. And when they ran out of wine, the mother of Jesus said to Him, "They have no wine." Jesus said to her, "Woman, what does your concern have to do with Me? My hour has not yet come." His mother said to the servants, "Whatever He says to you, do it." Now there were set there six waterpots of stone, according to the manner of purification of the Jews, containing twenty or thirty gallons apiece. Jesus said to them, "Fill the waterpots with water." And they filled them up to the brim. And He said to them, "Draw some out now, and take it to the master of the feast." And they took it. When the master of the feast had tasted the water that was made wine and did not know where it came from (but the servants who had drawn the water knew), the master of the feast called the bridegroom. And he said to him, "Every man at the beginning sets out the good wine, and when the guests have well drunk, then the inferior. You have kept the good wine until now!" This beginning of signs Jesus did in Cana of Galilee and manifested His glory, and His disciples believed in Him.

This was a wonderful thing Jesus did for the wedding party. He cared about the wedding and didn't want the celebration to fail or be spoken of badly. Jesus cares about the smallest to the greatest of details in all our lives. If you have any seemingly small detail of something in your life, you can be assured that Jesus cares about that. He will work things out for you no matter how big or how small.

This next miracle is a strange miracle. One that if a modern man was to perform this one, we would think it very strange and wonder if it was even godly. But Jesus does things by His own will and way. When you need a miracle, you won't dictate how it comes, you will just be glad it came. Let's look at another miracle.

Jesus Spits in the Mud: John 9:5-11 *(NKJV)*

As long as I am in the world, I am the light of the world." When He had said these things, He spat on the ground and made clay with the saliva; and

He anointed the eyes of the blind man with the clay. And He said to him, "Go, wash in the pool of Siloam" (which is translated, Sent). So, he went and washed, and came back seeing. Therefore, the neighbors and those who previously had seen that he was blind said, "Is not this he who sat and begged?" Some said, "This is he." Others said, "He is like him." He said, "I am he." Therefore, they said to him, "How were your eyes opened?" He answered and said, "A Man called Jesus made clay and anointed my eyes and said to me, 'Go to the pool of Siloam and wash.' So, I went and washed, and I received sight."

Wow! What a miracle that was! Right? Jesus is so creative. I don't think you or I could have come up with that idea to heal someone. Do you think you know anyone today that would even let you put spit-mud on their eyes? I don't think so, but God can.

I think this last miracle is incredible because Jesus did something that was really forbidden. You never touch a person with leprosy. Never. But Jesus did. He touched this man and healed him. I think this miracle tells you that no matter how dirty you think you are or broken or messed up you are not too far gone for Jesus to touch you.

Jesus Heal a Man with Leprosy: Mathew 8:1-4 *(NKJV)*

"When He had come down from the mountain, great multitudes followed Him. And behold, a leper came and worshiped Him, saying, 'Lord, if You are willing, You can make me clean.' Then Jesus put out His hand and touched him, saying, 'I am willing; be cleansed.' Immediately his leprosy was cleansed. And Jesus said to him, 'See that you tell no one; but go your way, show yourself to the priest, and offer the gift that Moses commanded, as a testimony to them.'"

If Jesus was willing to help heal the leper, He is also ready to heal you from any diseases and afflictions with which you are dealing. All you must do is ask Him to heal you and be with you, and He will take care of the rest.

Let me share with you two more strange miracles of Jesus.

We all know that Jesus raised the dead. This miracle is important because the religious leader came to Jesus asking for a miracle. I think the profound thing about this is Jesus said the girl wasn't dead but sleeping. I don't know about you but when a person dies, they are dead. But not to Jesus. When He announced this the people laughed at Jesus. Can you imagine someone laughing at Jesus?

Jesus Heals a Man's Dead Daughter: Mathew 9:18, 23-25 *(NIV)*

While he was saying this, a synagogue leader came and knelt before him and said, "My daughter has just died. But come and put your hand on her, and she will live." When Jesus entered the synagogue leader's house and saw the noisy crowd and people playing pipes, he said, "Go away. The girl is not dead but asleep." But they laughed at him. After the crowd had been put outside, he went in and took the girl by the hand, and she got up.

When He told the people in the house to leave and that the girl wasn't dead, but sleeping, they probably were shocked. It also says that they laughed at Jesus when He told them the girl wasn't dead. We can use this scripture as a stark reminder to not laugh at God the way these people did in this story. Instead, we can learn to laugh in obedience to God.

Jesus Heals a Blind Man at Bethsaida: Mark 8:22-26 *(NIV)*

They came to Bethsaida, and some people brought a blind man and begged Jesus to touch him. He took the blind man by the hand and led him outside the village. When he had spit on the man's eyes and put his hands on him, Jesus asked, "Do you see anything?" He looked up and said, "I see people; they look like trees walking around." Once more Jesus put his hands on the man's eyes. Then his eyes were opened, his sight was restored, and he saw everything clearly. Jesus sent him home, saying, "Don't even go into the village."

This was a strange miracle. Can you handle someone spitting on your eyes to heal them? I think not! But that is what Jesus did. Jesus healed the blind man and told him not to go into the village that he was near to protect him from harm. How much more should we listen to God when He tells us to do something or when He tells us not to do something?

Remember, Jesus knows more than we can ever think of or fathom, and He knows how to best intervene for all of our sakes. There is nothing Jesus doesn't know. So, if He ever speaks to us telling us to do something or not to do something, we should be listening intently. God does unusual miracles even today.

These miracles of Jesus are amazing! They are life-changing to the people that received them. Jesus wants you and me to do miracles just like these and more. You have the faith to release miracles for the sick and lost as well. The people that need you to release a miracle are in desperate need and when they get one their lives will forever be changed.

When I attended School of Ministry, Heidi Baker would sometimes come and speak. One of my favorite sayings she would share was this: "It's not complicated. Just love the one in front of you." So that is what we did and still are doing! Let me show you how.

Double Miracle

When I was ministering in Brazil, a woman named Rose shared her amazing miracle testimony with me. But God is so good, He had even more for her during my time there! She shared with me that at fifteen years old, she had been hit by a car and died. She saw Jesus and He brought her back to life. As she was recuperating from her injuries in the hospital, the doctors told her she would never be able to walk or have children. However, the doctors were wrong. Rose was able to walk and eventually had two children.

The accident had left her with one leg two centimeters shorter than the other. The whole ordeal also led to pain that would last for twenty-five years Until...Jesus! At the house where I was staying, several of us with the pastor decided to pray for Rose. Several people gathered around Rose and began to pray and speak to the leg to grow out. God heard and moved! We all watched in amazement as her shorter leg grew out. Her legs were now the same length, and all her pain was gone! She said, "My God is a God of miracles, there are no limits to His power to act, He does the impossible, for Him nothing is too difficult." Rose later shared that since her amazing healing at the conference, she was able to begin walking for an hour a day and she even started going to the gym every other day. She shared, "I'm now doing exercises that I couldn't before. I'm very happy! Glory to God...!"

Ministering To People at Disneyland:

We took a team of about twenty people to Disneyland to minister love and healing to people. A few years before, a group of friends went to Disneyland to minister and came back to share amazing testimonies that inspired us to do the same. We decided to hang out and play at Disney and were very excited to see what the Lord would do. We decided to be very intentional about going out and loving people.

We got there and believed that the opportunities would be abundant. But we purposed to be led and be very intentional about going out and loving on people when God gave us the opportunity. So, sure enough, we got there, and God opened doors for us.

The first lady came walking up, and she was pushing another lady in a wheelchair. Yes! Wheelchair time is awesome, and we sensed it was time to get people out of them. We had prayed before we went that God would get people out of wheelchairs while we were at Disneyland. So, we prayed for her. She needed the wheelchair. She had been using it due to the pain in her legs. She couldn't walk around; she couldn't do anything at Disneyland. She didn't need the wheelchair all the time, but she did need it to get around Disneyland. After praying for her, she got out of the wheelchair and walked. She could walk on her ankle, which used to be injured, without any pain. She no longer needed the wheelchair!

She got out of the chair and said, "Yes! This is awesome!"

We knew God wanted to do more. We ended up praying for four people that had been in wheelchairs that day. One of them was a man whose name was Jesus (yes, Jesus was in a wheelchair), and his father was pushing him. The father saw his son get completely healed, and they gave their hearts to Jesus right there that day at Disneyland!

We had crazy miracles happening that day.

Then we decided to get on a water ride. We start talking to this lady in line, prophesying and praying over her. It was so incredible because her boyfriend worked at Disneyland too. We found out later that the other team was over in another area of Disneyland, already prophesying and praying over her boyfriend.

Do you know that she ended up giving her heart to Jesus? That is what her boyfriend had been praying for. See, God wants to use us more than we want to be used. It doesn't matter where you are. Whether at the grocery store, hospital, Disneyland, or church. Be available to God and watch Him get people out of wheelchairs through your hands.

Continued Miracles

Do you know the world is crying out for joy and miracles? The world needs a touch from Jesus. They are hurting now more than ever. If you continue to laugh and use your gift of laughter you can be that vessel that Jesus uses for others. The laughter you use means that something in the spirit realm is being released. Let it be released for the people in front of you God sends you to. They are not crossing your path by accident.

Let me tell you how bad the world is crying out for joy. I've researched this and have been cultivating and stewarding this gift for over ten years. I'm not going to tell you that I have never had another tear. That would be a lie! As I shared in the previous chapter, I went through a seven-month period that was one of the most challenging seasons of my life. Even in the excruciating pain and tears dripping down my face, the Lord kept saying to me, "Laugh."

I want to share this testimony that happened on the Sundial Bridge. It is amazing. I love when testimonies or miracles happen. It starts a domino effect. We were down at the Sundial Bridge. There were several groups of people going out and loving on people. I walked up with a couple of other people to a gentleman who had a brace on his knee. It was obvious he had knee issues.

We walked up to him and said, "Hey. We are out loving on people. Is it possible that we can pray for you?"

At first, he wasn't too sure about it, and then he said, "Yeah, you can pray for my knee."

So, we prayed for his knee, and I asked if he was in pain.

He said, "Yes, of course, I am in pain. It is bone on bone all the time."

We prayed for it, and we just prayed that God would give him a new knee. He just looked at us like we were crazy, but we just continued to pray for him and release joy over him.

Then I asked, "Is there any way you can check it out?"

He snickered at us.

"No, actually, this is a huge contraption I have on my knee, and it is going to take a while to take off."

I said, "OK, well then the next time you take it off, just check it out and see if it feels any better."

We left the man knowing that we had gone out, and we released God's love. That's what we are called to do. Just go out and love on people. Leave the results to Jesus.

We walked away after we blessed him.

There was another friend of mine that we walked up on, and they were praying for someone in a wheelchair. Suddenly, this lady they were praying for got up out of her wheelchair and began to walk with a cane that her husband was holding next to her. She was in a wheelchair, then went to a cane, and soon, she was walking across the Sundial Bridge.

In the meantime, we left to find other people just to bless and pour God's love on. We were praying for a guy underneath a gazebo who was battling brain cancer. We began to pray for him. As we were praying for him another guy walked up to us.

As he walks up, I start jumping up and down. I was like a little kid. I was so excited. I was jumping up and down and laughing, and the rest of the team was looking at me like, what is she doing? But what they didn't see is I saw the gentleman come walking towards us, that we had prayed for earlier and he was carrying that knee brace contraption over his head.

And he said, "My knee was completely better."

We all got so excited, we said, "Praise Jesus, this is awesome!"

And, when he came up to us, we asked him if he needed more healing. We asked if he had shoulder pain.

He said, "Actually, I have a torn rotator cuff. Can you please pray for it?"

We prayed, and the first time nothing happened. So, we prayed again, and the second time nothing happened. Then we prayed a third time, and do you know nothing happened? And guess what, we continued a fourth, fifth, sixth, and seventh time.

How many of you would have stopped? Now we are praying eight times praying for the same person and not seeing any results, not seeing any breakthrough. Finally, it was only the ninth time, and right before he received his miracle, his wife said, "I'll believe it when I see it." So, the ninth time we prayed, we declared healing into his arm.

Suddenly, he lifts his arm, and the torn rotator cuff is completely healed. And his wife's jaw dropped, and she said, "Oh my gosh, I cannot believe what I am seeing."

That day, because of that miracle, she ended up giving her heart to Jesus.

That wasn't the end because, as I said, "the domino effect" was in effect. His healing didn't just affect him. It affected everyone who was around him. He wasn't healed immediately. It took nine times of prayers for his rotator cuff to be completely healed. And when you are out and around people, it's just, God's love that oozes over people. It's His love that heals people.

We announced that we were doing miracles for the people there.

"Hey, God is doing miracles right now. So, if you need a miracle, come here right now because God wants to touch you."

It is the testimony of Jesus as the Spirit of prophecy, so take these testimonies as you read this book. If you know anyone who has a knee issue or shoulder issue, and you pray for them don't quit. You know God will use you and God is faithful to your prayers.

Sometimes you will have to press in and get the healing. You will have to pray more than once. That is okay. This one time, it took nine times for this man to get his miracle, but the biggest miracle was his wife gave her heart to Jesus!

Carpel Tunnel Miracle

Here is another testimony about me to increase your faith.

I had lived with a debilitating condition for ten years in both hands from the repetitive work I did in the airlines. I had been to many doctors and had many tests, needles, and even several surgeries to alleviate the pain, but nothing worked. They were all just a temporary fix for this condition. Here I was, thirty years old, in what felt like an eighty-year-old body.

I had been first diagnosed with carpal tunnel and tendonitis in my hands. Then, after having a chance to see a good renowned hand surgeon who had taught others about hand surgery, I was told that I had thoracic outlet syndrome.

I said, "OK, now that we know what the problem is, how can we fix it?"

The hand specialist told me that it could only be fixed with surgery, but the doctors warned me the odds were not in my favor.

They told me, "There is a thirty-three percent chance you will get better, a thirty-three percent chance you will stay the same, and a thirty-three percent chance you will get worse."

With those odds, I decided I would just live with the condition. I did, however, eventually decide to have the surgery on my left hand only. It did seem to help make my left hand feel better. However, I was still dealing with terrible pain and tingling in my right hand.

Everything took longer to do, from washing dishes to cleaning my house. What would take some people only an hour or two to clean their house would take me twice as long. I always wore a glove or a splint on my hand even after having the surgery. I couldn't lift my children. They learned how to climb up my side so I could hold them. I was always in pain and dealing with pins and needles every day in my hands. To add to the condition, my right hand was always cold. I couldn't write for long periods, so in college, they would make an announcement on the first day of school asking if someone could take notes for me. I felt so embarrassed that this was the only way to get a note-taker in college. I also had the state pay for a note-taker, but that eventually became too expensive.

To write my papers, I would have to use a program on the computer that would type all my words, but it didn't work half of the time and just made it more challenging. I also had to take a recorder into class to re-listen to the teaching since some people who took notes didn't take the notes very well. I would still have to take them for myself.

Folding laundry would take days instead of hours as my hands would get so tired, and the pain was so great that I would have to keep stopping. This was my life, and I had settled that I would just have to learn how to live with the condition. Until Jesus came and changed everything.

I woke up one morning and heard an audible voice tell me to pull weeds. It was about 6:00 a.m., and I said, "What? No way!"

"First, it is too early; 6:00 a.m.! Are you kidding? Second, I hate pulling weeds; and third, I can't because of my hands."

I heard the voice again say, "Go pull weeds."

So, I got up, and since my mom was visiting my son and me, I shared with her about my encounter. She was no help to me, or so I thought. She said, "I should read Matthew 13:24-43. It's all about the parable of the weeds." I told her, "I would read it."

I read the parable and still had no understanding of what that verse had to do with me going out and physically pulling weeds. Except that it had been a couple of months, the quarter-acre land we lived on had quite a few weeds since no one had been maintaining them for the last few months. So, I bargained with God. Yes, you read that right. I negotiated with God.

I said, "OK, I will go pull weeds at 9:00 a.m."

That was when my son would be leaving with his grandma to spend a few days with her. My daughter was already in the area visiting her other grandparents. Sure enough, as soon as 9:00 a.m. hit, I loaded my son in the car, and it started to rain.

I said aloud, "Praise Jesus, I don't have to go pull weeds since it is raining."

Then, my mom chimed in and said, "the rain makes the ground softer, making it easier to pull weeds." So, I waved goodbye to my mom and son and went and put on my coat to pull weeds. I was not happy. I was yelling at God as I was also angry. My husband had just left me, and there I was with this debilitating condition pulling weeds. Yes, you could say I was having an adult temper tantrum. My life was in shambles, and I pulled weeds in the pouring rain. I felt I was at the lowest place I had ever been in. A week before this, I contemplated suicide, so to now be out pulling weeds felt like the lowest of lows.

I wasn't out there for minutes. It was a few hours. I forgot to ask how long I needed to pull weeds in all my negotiating with God. So, I cried, yelled, and pulled weeds in the rain for hours. I came in drenched from the rain. The next morning, I woke up, and I desired to pull weeds, unlike the day before. I couldn't wait to pull weeds. I grabbed my CD player and went out and started pulling weeds. I was out there for hours again.

This time I was singing to my music and having fun pulling weeds. Every day I would spend hours out there pulling weeds. I continued to worship as I pulled weeds for the next four days. Remember, I lived on a quarter of an acre of land, so I had plenty to keep busy. Every day there was an excitement to go and pull weeds.

I hadn't realized the biggest miracle that I had not even asked for had already happened. I went to church on Friday, and for the first time, I was able to lift my hands and worship without any pain or tingling. I thought this was strange. I still did not know that I was healed. The next day, I drove down to pick up my children after they had been gone for a week, and the first thing my son said to me was, "Mom, your hand is warm."

That was when I realized I had been healed. My son had never felt my hand warm since he was born, nor had my daughter, as I had this condition before they were born. I knew God had healed me at that moment, so I told my children what God had done.

Since then, I have had no pain in my hands. I continued my college endeavors and received my bachelor's degree without any more note-takers. Here I am, twenty-one years later, writing a book. That is the power of God! He healed my hands when I didn't even ask Him to! I believe this because I was obedient but had a lot of resistance. But God never gave up on me. Despite my ugly attitude toward Him, He still chose not only to heal my hands but also my heart. He gave me a hunger to know Him, go worldwide, and share His goodness with everyone I meet.

My story reminded me of the story in the Bible where the soldier of the King had leprosy. He went out to see the King of Israel for his healing. When the word got back to Elisha, the prophet, that the King of Israel was in distress over a soldier from another King that was asking for healing, Elisha sent a messenger to tell the soldier to dip in the Jordan river seven times, and he would be healed.

However, the Jordan River was the dirtiest. Then Naaman got angry because he thought he would be healed differently. He thought with just the wave of a hand, he would be healed. He didn't think he had to do anything to instigate his healing. So, he walked away from his healing. He even inquired if he could dip in another clean river, not the dirtiest river in the land. It was only when a servant of the soldier implored him to go and dip in the river that he chose to get in.

After he dipped in the river seven times, a miracle happened. This man who had a debilitating disease was completely healed; his skin renewed to a little boy's skin. The miracle happened by doing something that he felt was beneath him and, in his eyes, degrading.

What would have happened if he had not listened to his servant? What would his life have been like living with leprosy his entire life? We won't ever know since he chose to listen and obey, even if it was reluctantly.

See, there was one part of my story I had left out when I was young. If we got in trouble as kids one of our punishments was to have to go and pull weeds. I would be given a spoon to help dig out the roots and pull weeds. So, when I was asked to pull weeds, by God, that seemed to be the worst thing anyone could have asked me to do. But it was God using that to heal my debilitating condition and free me from years of pain.

Thank you, Jesus, for never giving up on me even when I did it, screaming and yelling the whole way. Just like the soldier in the Bible, I will never know what it feels like to live with the debilitating condition since I chose to trust God and go pull weeds. God is good all the time.

Godly Lifestyle Activation

The Bible isn't just a history of things that happened in the past, but it is a love letter from God about how we can live a fulfilled life and that includes laughter. He has shown us many times how important laughter and joy are in the Bible and still are today for breakthroughs in our lives.

God's Truth

> ➤ If you have any sickness or disease, it is biblical to ask for prayer for healing from others.

"Is anyone among you sick? Let him call for the elders of the church, and let them pray over him, anointing him with oil in the name of the Lord. 15 And the prayer of faith will save the sick, and the Lord will raise him up. And if he has committed sins, he will be forgiven." - James 5:14-15 NKJV

> ➤ We can stand on His word and trust His never-ending and never-failing promises. He has given us the authority to overcome all the enemy's power. He doesn't say some or few. He says all authority to overcome the enemy has been given to us.

"Behold, I give you the authority to trample on serpents and scorpions, and over all the power of the enemy, and nothing shall by any means hurt you."
- Luke 10:19 NKJV

> ➤ The woman believed that she would be healed if she could only touch Jesus's garment. As a result, we can learn a lot about her faith in God, and we can teach ourselves to have that same type of faith.

"Now a certain woman had a flow of blood for twelve years and had suffered many things from many physicians. She had spent all that she had and was no better, but rather grew worse. When she heard about Jesus, she came behind Him in the crowd and touched His garment. For she said, 'If only I may touch His clothes, I shall be made well.' Immediately the fountain of her

blood was dried up, and she felt in her body that she was healed of the affliction." - Mark 5:25-29 NKJV

Your Response to God's Truth

Write down on a small piece of paper a sickness or situation you need a breakthrough in. Then place it in your shoe and throughout the day laugh every time you think about the difficulty. Try this for a week and see what happens.

Ask a Christian friend, elder, or pastor to laugh with you over your situation sometime this week.

Scriptures for Further Study:

"Who Himself bore our sins in His own body on the tree, that we, having died to sins, might live for righteousness—by whose stripes you were healed."
- 1 Peter 2:24 NKJV

"Heal me, O Lord, and I shall be healed; Save me, and I shall be saved, For You are my praise-Jeremiah 17:14 NKJV

"O my soul, you have said to the Lord, "You are my Lord, my goodness is nothing apart from You." - Psalm 16:2 NKJV

"Beloved, I pray that you may prosper in all things and be in health, just as your soul prospers." - 3 John 1:2 NKJV

"Preserve me, O God, for in You I put my trust. O, my soul, you have said to the Lord You are my Lord, my goodness is nothing apart from You." - Psalm 16:1-2 NKJV

CHAPTER NINE

Miracles Through Laughter

Testimonies are powerful. They help us to see that the good thing that happened to someone else is possible for us. I love testimonies and you will love these that I share with you in this chapter.

Let's start calling forth those things and saying, "Yes, I take this as my own." Because testimonies have power, and they are not just private for one person. Jesus said, *"And they overcame him by the blood of the Lamb and by the word of their testimony."- Revelation 12:11 NKJV*

What if we never heard any testimonies about Jesus? We would not know our inheritance. If Mathew, Mark, Luke, John, and Paul had not written anything down, we would never understand what we really possess in Christ. We would never know that we are commissioned to heal the sick, raise the dead, cast out demons, and cleanse the lepers. We would never have imagined that it was possible. But it is possible.

Years ago, people used to tell me, "Kristina, I see intercession all over you." I would think, "Augh! Not intercession!" In my heart, that was hard work, so I refused to even consider it. But when I learned that laughter was intercession, my heart leaped. Everything changed. It was as if I had been created for this thing called laughter or the prophetic intercession of laughter.

I want to share with you some very real testimonies of life-changing events because of what laughter has done in the lives of individuals. They gave me permission to share their stories so you can see for yourself what the power of laughter can bring.

I pray that you take these testimonies as your own and claim them over your life and the lives of people around you. Pray them over your family and friends and claim them as your own in Jesus' mighty name. Remember how I said the testimonies of Jesus are the spirit of prophecy? So, if you know anyone with knee issues, back issues, or shoulder issues, proclaim in Jesus' name that they will be healed.

Migraine Healed

Chris and his wife from Arizona, were on a phone call with me.

Chris: *"We wanted to share our testimonies and the amazing things God has done in our lives.*

It was a year ago in April. April 26, 2012 just prior to that, God had given me a dream of a blonde-haired woman coming in, and she wanted to talk to my wife, and it was kind of like confusing, and then a few days later Kristina showed up, and I turned around at the School of Supernatural Ministry in Arizona, and when she came to the door I looked over and said, "That is a woman from the dream. Then later that night, when one of her team members asked, "Has anyone here had migraines?" And no one raised their hands. I raised my hand and said, "My wife does. She has had migraines for 37 years," and Kristina said, "Can you get her on the cell phone?" So, is that how she is going to talk to her? Do you know? Because it was kind of confusing at first. Then I will let my wife tell you what happened next."

Wife: *"So, I got home, and I am in bed. I have had migraines since I was fourteen. At the time, I was fifty. So, the phone rings, and I did not want to answer the phone. I am in bed with a horrible migraine, and I am saying to myself that I am not answering the phone. But I finally picked up the phone because it was ringing relentlessly. So, Chris was like, we want to pray with you. I'm like; I don't want to talk. I didn't want to talk, but we started praying, and I just started having this feeling like, gosh, something is moving, and there was like this tingling, and I just started feeling this amazing, just amazingness. This movement just started happening, and it was just amazing!"*

Chris: *"You said you felt it come down both your arms?"*

Wife: *"Yes, it was like this feeling just started moving all over me, and we just kept praying."*

Kristina: *"How were they praying?"*

Wife: *"They were laughing, so much laughing, and we just kept praying and laughing; a lot of laughing. The pain just started to subside. Like I said, the tingling, and the pain just started to subside, and I am like this is just amazing! By the time we got off the phone, the pain was gone. The next morning, I went grocery shopping for the first time without a headache. It has been absolutely amazing since then. I have been able to work full-time, which I had never been able to do. I work in surgery, and our lives have been turned around! It has absolutely been a miracle for us! I have been working actually more than full time."*

Husband: *"Yes, she is driving an hour each way to work, where before she couldn't even work two or three days a week, and she would miss like ninety days."*

Wife: *"Yes, I lost my job before that because of headaches."*

Husband: *"Yes, now she has been in this job for fourteen or fifteen months. She missed one day because she had stomach flu."*

Wife: *"Yes."*

Kristina: *"You never knew her without migraines?"*

Chris: *"No. No, when I met her, she had migraines. I mean, it was a common occurrence for her to like be puking her guts out on a regular basis."*

Kristina: *"And your children too?"*

Chris and his wife: *"Yes, we have one daughter. She has never known her mom not to have just horrible headaches all the time! So, it has just been a new life for us. We don't know. We never knew what it was like not to have headaches all the time. So, it has been a new life for us."*

Kristina: *"Thank you, Jesus!"*

Wife: *"We have been restored, our life has been restored, and we give all the glory to the Lord!"*

Kristina: *"And you are now facilitators?"*

Chris: *"Yes, at the school at the supernatural school here in Arizona."*

Kristina: *"And you do treasure hunts?"*

Chris: *"Yes, my wife has gone with us. We (my daughter and family) go out and do treasure hunts, and God just leads us to people. We have seen people have their knees* *healed, their backs healed. We saw a few months back. We got a report about a man we prayed for in the hospital who had stage three stomach cancer who when they tried to do chemo, he couldn't do chemo because he couldn't tolerate it at all, so they took him off of it immediately! Then went back like eight weeks later to wait for him to be strong enough to do the surgery, and they went ahead and did scans to see the progression of the cancer. In fact, even before that, the next day, they were doing tests, and they said after we prayed, and then they said, "well, it looks like stage two cancer, now. Then eight weeks later, they turned around, and he was strong enough to do surgery. So, they went and did scans, and they couldn't find the cancer!"*

Kristina: *"Yes, God!"*

Husband: *"Then they did biopsies, and they couldn't find any cancer cells."*

Kristina: *"So, can you just release healing over the video right now? Just anybody with migraines or any kind of sickness? Can you just release?"*

Husband: *"Yes, we just open up heaven right now. We pour out heaven to everyone watching this video. To everybody who has suffered with migraines, we command those migraines to leave right now. We command pain to go right now in the name of Jesus! Completely, completely in the name of Jesus!"*

Husband and wife: *"Thank you, Jesus! We give you all the glory, Jesus!"*

Kristina: *Amen! Bless you, guys."*

Woman Healed

On a ministry trip, I spoke at a women's conference in a small city in California. It was Friday night, we called out words of knowledge and people's names. As God dropped the name "Tracey" in my mind. I asked everybody if they knew anyone named Tracey.

"Does anyone have the name, Tracey? Does that name mean anything to anyone?" No one raised their hand. Clearly, I missed something.

But God was really calling her. So, the very next day, when the women's conference began, another pastor spoke, and she began praying for this woman. When the pastor asked her what her name was, she replied, "My name is Tracey."

"Oh, Kristina has a word for you," the pastor said.

As we made declarations, she explained how she was having trouble just standing up and doing what everyone else was doing.

The other pastor asked my team and me to go and pray for her. We prayed for her and discovered that she is blind in one eye, deaf in one ear, and has no feeling in one leg. Only through muscle memory, she knew how to walk, and her left arm was numb. She couldn't feel anything when you touched her. We started praying for her, then we prophesied over her. She went down in the Spirit, and we began singing, *"God is so good."* When she opened her eyes, she said, "I see light."

We were excited because she couldn't see light in that eye before, and then she could. So, we asked her to close her eyes again, and then I heard the song, *"He Knows My Name."*

God must have known her name because He had called her since the night before, so we began singing that song.

As we sang, *"He Knows Your Name,* Tracey. He knows your every thought. He sees each tear you've cried. He hears you when you call."

She said that as we continued to sing and heard my voice, she felt the sound pierce inside her ear, followed by a sensation that radiated throughout her body. After that, her body came alive from the inside out.

Later she shared that song was actually the song she would hear in her darkest moments. This was the work of the Holy Spirit since we did not know her. Then she stood up and said, "I can see, I can see!"

We all got excited, so everyone prayed for her ears, and then her ear opened up. Then I said, "You should dance." Pretty soon, she was doing the swing dance. She had not been able to do anything for two and a half years. Her face had been paralyzed. But now she was a miracle, and she wasn't paralyzed!

Following the service, we went out to lunch. Tracey was sitting in front of a tree, and the tree kept rubbing against her arm. For the first time in two and a half years, she felt the tree scratching her arm and she just let it happen because she said, "I haven't felt anything in two and a half years."

The reason God uses testimonies is so He can do it again. It is to give you all encouragement that He can do it again. So, if you know of anyone with paralysis, anyone who is deaf in one ear, or anyone who is blind, then take these testimonies because God wants to heal other people.

According to the Bible, the Spirit of prophecy is the testimony of Jesus. That means He wants to do it again, and He wants to do it through you. The following is another incredible story of perseverance in the face of seemingly hopeless circumstances. This occurred when I was leading what we called "treasure hunts."

Treasure hunts are where we would go out, follow clues, and find people. But, throughout the two weeks I had been doing this, every single place we went, we were told no by the people we met. No one was interested in talking to us. Usually, you can at least talk to someone. But unfortunately, nobody wanted to speak to us. Have you ever felt like the grace in your life to accomplish something has ended? This is that kind of story.

My mistake was believing a lie. I accepted a lie that God's grace for me to go out into the world and love people was over. How ridiculous is that? Right?

Broken Wrist Healed

Walmart was our next stop to reach out to people. Our question was, "Hey, do you have any pain in your body? Because God wants to heal you!" However, everyone said "no."

Then we're down to the last fifteen minutes of our treasure hunt. I'd already decided beforehand that this would probably be my last and final treasure hunt. But, since there had been no results, I felt like I was beating my head against the same wall and just wanted to give up.

I'm the group leader, so I know my team will react based on how I react. Now I'm trying to have a good attitude, knowing it's probably going to be the last time. Suddenly, I saw this lady wearing a pink jacket, and I remember someone on our team had a pink jacket.

So, I said, "Look, a woman is wearing a pink jacket. Let's go talk to her."

Someone said, "She's got red hair, and my little map says I am looking for someone with blond hair."

My response was, "Well, ignore the map, forget about her hair color, look at her arm, and she's wearing a wrist brace or an ace bandage around her wrist."

A guy was walking behind her, and he was limping, and I had a "shorter leg" on my map. So, we walked up to them. It is important to understand that I have no confidence in my ability to help these people in any way whatsoever. At that time, I decided that I would never do this again. So, I'm just doing this to go out with a bang.

I said, "Hey, we're out loving on people," when I approached them. "We're on this treasure hunt. Would it be okay if we prayed for you?" I expected to hear the word "no."

You should have seen my face when she said "yes." I said, "Really?"

In other words, I was shocked! For two or three weeks, there was nothing but "no"; it was constantly "no, no, no, no."

I asked her what was wrong. She told me that her wrist was broken.

I asked, "Are you in pain?"

"Yes," she replied, and I asked, "What is your pain level?"

She said, "Oh, it's about an eight." The pain was nearly unbearable, so we prayed and laughed over her, and the pain started to subside.

In the meantime, I asked the man with her what was happening in his life that he needed prayers for.

He said, "Well, I was injured in a motorcycle accident years ago, and I've been in pain ever since."

I said, "Well, what is your pain level?" And he said, "Fifteen."

That's excruciating.

So, I told him, "As soon as we are done praying for her, we will pray for you." I didn't realize he was her son. After we prayed for this lady, her pain level is at a three, and she puts the other wrist out. I asked her what was wrong with her other wrist.

After we prophesied over her, we started calling out her destiny and reminding her who she was. Finally, she said, "Well, I'm a cook, and I've got arthritis in this hand."

We began praying and speaking life over her wrist. After I prayed, I had no faith whatsoever, none to even say, "Hey, why don't you test it out?" You first check out what God is doing because you want to give Him praise and glory. The next thing I know, she takes her purse and lifts it with her thumb; the thumb with the ace bandage on it. You know, if you have a broken wrist, you can't lift your thumb without experiencing pain, and she was acting like there was no pain.

Our reaction was, "Oh, praise God!"

Now I think, "Wahoo. I get to go out with a bang!" So, then I went to her son and said, "Can we pray for you?"

He was talking to his wife on the phone, and he said, "Actually when you were praying for my mom, all the pain left me. I don't know who you are, but can you please pray for my wife right now? She's on the phone." We prayed for his wife, and she began to feel God's presence.

After the phone conversation ended, I asked the woman again, and she replied, "I will remove the ace bandage when I get home."

There was no faith in me even to ask her to do anything, try it out, or test it; nothing. The truth is, it's not about us anyway, right? It's all about Jesus. We must have faith in our heavenly Father. Knowing that He is good all the time ought to be enough for us. The lady mentioned she was scheduled to have surgery three days later. However, the doctor was waiting for the swelling to go down before performing the surgery.

Suddenly, she exclaimed, "You know what? I'm taking off my bandage right now!"

I watched as she started carefully unraveling the two bandages that had been around her wrist. She threw them both into her shopping cart and asked me, "Would you like these?"

"Really?" I asked. Yes!"

It is powerful to give God glory and recognize what He's done.

I said, "Sure. I'll take them!"

The next thing I knew, she was moving and shaking her wrists. Then, she made this ungodly noise, and I thought, "Oh no!" I am in big trouble!" That wasn't a pretty sound!

I asked her, "Are you in pain right now?"

She replied, "Yeah, but I'm not in pain anymore!"

She moved her wrists in circles, and it was evident that she was completely healed. For me, it was significant because it occurred at a time when I didn't have anything to give. The Bible says that *"So I am well pleased with weaknesses, with insults, with distresses, with persecutions, and with difficulties, for the sake of Christ; for when I am weak [in human strength], then I am strong [truly able, truly powerful, truly drawing from God's strength]."- 2 Corinthians 12:10 AMP*

In an unlikely place like Walmart, Jesus showed up and showed off when I thought there was nothing else to give. As a result of that situation, I realized I believed a lie. I was planning on attending the School of Ministry that day, so I wore them around my neck like trophies. People approached me and asked, "Hey, what is going on? Why are you wearing those?" I would happily respond, "Look what Jesus did today!"

I went to the School of Ministry that day and met up with a friend and told him how I was feeling. This person was leading this outreach with me, so I gave him a bandage and said, "I think one of these is for you." He asked, "Hey, will you do me a favor and write the testimony of what happened at Walmart on this bandage?" So, I wrote it down for him.

God used a testimony written on an Ace bandage from a healing in Walmart that happened when we didn't think we had anything left to give. God is so good! People have shared this Ace bandage story over and over again. Others have taken that testimony as their own and seen the same and even more outstanding results than the ones we have seen.

Christ in you is the hope of glory. Your hope doesn't come from how you feel or what you think. It comes from Christ alone. Sometimes we have to do things we don't want to do. Hebrews 13:15 *NKJV* urges us to *"continually offer the sacrifice of praise to God."*

Everything changes when we worship and give God glory. And there may be times that you are sacrificing with tears dripping down your face.

But in those times, you can choose joy. It's a choice. Throughout this book, you will read testimonies of people who chose joy over pain. In their pain, they abandoned their place of comfort to turn to the One who could replace it with joy and peace.

Back Issues Healed

That same afternoon, my friend was at a gas station with the ace bandage in hand with his youngest son. He had the testimony. The proof was there of what God had done.

As he entered the gas station, he held up the ace bandage and asked, "Does anyone want to know why I am holding this up?" Two women approached him and asked, "Yeah, why?"

When he began to share what happened, he asked, "Are you feeling pain in your body? Because God wants to heal you just as He healed this lady." He and his son prayed for two or three ladies. Two of them were healed of back issues, and one gave her heart to Jesus.

Family Restored

Here is another amazing testimony. There was a couple who had problems in their relationship. The guy's mom had laughed over their relationship and interceded on their behalf two days before the couple ended up going to church together. Then the next day, he went to church, and then on Sunday morning, they were both in church for the first time in five years.

They were getting ready to end their marriage. So, we went to church and got a chance to minister to each of them separately. Remember, before that, the man's mother had laughed over their situation. We were all together, and I said, "I just want you to see that mountain in front of you and I want you to start laughing over it."

And so, she starts laughing, and she sees her children. She wants their marriage to succeed. This was all on Friday night. Then on Saturday, we connected with them. We ended up just being able to love on them and speak life into them. On Sunday, which happened to be Mother's Day, the son comes to church for the first time in five years. The son came to church, but he didn't just come. He brought his wife too. It was a good day. God allowed a mother's prayer to move mountains while she was laughing at the plans of the enemy and look at what God did! He brought that family back together. I've seen so many families restored through laughter because it is warfare.

I've also seen people get supernatural finances like crazy. At one Homegroup meeting, we had a lady share, "Well, I need my tuition paid," and she wrote down $1,310. We had written prayer requests on pieces of paper and passed them around to each other and we just started laughing over each one because we knew there was something about picking up the burdens of our brothers and sisters. We continued laughing, contending, and thanking God for what He was doing. Four days later, an anonymous person gave her $1,310. Her tuition was completely paid off. So, whatever your situation is, whatever you need God to do for you He will do it.

Missing Child Found

I have a heart for missing children. I have talked about it in my life many times. Believe it or not, we have laughed over missing children. When we find out a child is missing, we laugh. Now I know this probably doesn't sound the most biblical. But God says in 1 Corinthians 1:27 (*NIV*), *"But God chose the foolish things of the world to shame the wise; God chose the weak things of the world to shame the strong."* So, there was a missing child, and you know what? We laughed. We are just going to laugh because that is what God is doing. He is laughing at the plans of the enemy.

We got together, started laughing, and started watching the news. We started interceding. We started laughing. We kept watching the news. An Amber Alert never went out because the child was actually with a family member, however, the story of the missing child went national on Nancy's Show.

Then the next week, we laughed some more. We found out that the amount they were offering as a reward was $10,000. Then it jumped up to $100,000, and we were praising Jesus, and we started laughing some more.

The next week, they found the car, and we started praising Jesus and laughing even more.

Finally, the next week, we see a praise report that they had found the child. They found her on Mission Street in another city in California. The most incredible thing is, that they just didn't find her, they found another little girl because we had all these pictures. So, we were just laughing over missing children in general. There was a three-year-old little girl that had been missing from Virginia. She had been taken from her home, and they found her on Mission Street that same weekend!

There is power when you release laughter in situations. I know there is power, and God will use it in incredible ways. I can't tell you how often we have laughed over people and seen them completely restored.

Laughter Diffuses the Enemy's Plans

It doesn't matter what it is. Laughter isn't just for one type of problem. From sickness to protection, laughter covers it all.

The second time I was in South Africa, two gangs of older teens were getting ready to fight each other. They had rocks and giant bricks and were prepared to hurt each other. All of this happened as we were walking down the street. I told everyone on our team to start laughing, and we did. As we were laughing, they looked at us and each other like they were confused. Then they dropped their rocks and bricks, and each side yelled something to each other and walked away from each other. That's another example of the power of laughter. I saw it with my very own eyes because I was there.

Laughter Breaks Depression

I remember another lady named Pia. She had not laughed in fifty years. She gave her testimony at an event.

"Hi everyone, my name is Pia. I have never met Kristina before, and I am here at this meeting tonight. She was talking about laughing, and I was still skeptical because I hadn't laughed in such a long time. Then after a while, this whole laughter thing caught up with me, and it has been fifty years since I could remember the word laugh. Kristina piped in and confirmed that I had not laughed in fifty years. And suddenly I started laughing and laughing and laughing. The atmosphere above us, the demonic power that was upon us, had been broken up, and now I am going to put the words "ha, ha, ha, ha" all over my house. So there, Satan! Take this! See how it feels! Kristina asked me to release that joy and laughter over everybody who was watching. So, I started laughing again, ha, ha, ha, ha.

Then I said, "You guys got to laugh. You have to laugh! Continue to laugh. It's been so wonderful. For fifty years, my life had been a nightmare."

But I laughed some more, and there is no more pain. Thank you, Lord, thank you for sending Kristina. Thank you, Lord, and her name is Kristina because Christ is in her. In Jesus' name, amen.

So, if you need joy, start laughing; start laughing like you've never laughed before, and break that cloud of sickness, death, and disease around you. Laugh over anyone you know and speak life over yourself to get rid of it in Jesus' name, amen. -Pia

Hip Healed

God is so amazing, and I just thank God for Kristina coming. I am a worshiper. I came to play. But I didn't feel like coming. But I said, "Lord, I am just being obedient." My hip has been hurting for six months straight, and it was so bad I could barely walk sometimes, and I couldn't sleep most of the time. I would have to try to find a position to sleep in and I just couldn't deal with the pain. It got so bad I would have to stop for a while and think about what I was going to do or how I was going to walk. Long story short, after we did worship, I walked in there, and it was incredible. Kristina said, "OK, let's laugh at our problems."

So, everybody joined hands. We started laughing, and oh my gosh, I began to feel nothing but warm fire, and the next thing I know, the pain was completely gone.

We did worship again that night and amazingly God showed up miraculously just like He always does, and we give Him all the praise and the glory, and the pain has not come back. - Xavier

A Lady Diagnosed with Cancer

Another lady was fighting cancer, and she woke up in the middle of the night, to hear the Lord saying to her, "It is just a laughing matter."

She said, "But God, what about this? And what about this?"

God kept saying, "It's just a laughing matter."

And when I saw her the next day, her countenance had changed! She was a new woman. But I didn't get a chance to pray for her. As she stood before me, she suddenly fell on the ground. She had an encounter with Jesus. She sees Jesus coming to her, and He is shaking his head, and all He is saying to her "It's just a laughing matter."

She got so full of joy! You know if Jesus is saying "It is a laughing matter" then we should be doing the same thing. Because Jesus said, 'I only do what I see my Father doing' we get to do what we see our Father doing. If He is telling me to laugh at my problems, then guess what? We get a chance to laugh too.

The lady with cancer, as she is laughing, guess what she is producing? She is producing all kinds of immune cells. They are creating more and more and more inside her body. If you need an immune booster, instead of taking whatever little powder they put in your drink, just start laughing. That is the first immune booster you should take.

Kristina's Miracle with Her Two Children:

I have two children, and my daughter decided to go and live with her dad while she was in high school. Her dad, at the time, was a long way from California. She had lived with me her whole life until then. During this time, I didn't feel like laughing. I was broken over this news. But I knew I was called to laugh. However, laughter was not the first thing that I thought about doing, and matter of fact, my daughter moved out. For three days, I was in my bed, crying.

Finally, I said, "Lord, there is something wrong with this. You said I am supposed to be laughing, and I am not laughing. I am in bed crying. What is wrong with this picture?"

It is also good to surround yourself with people that will bring you back up and help encourage you because we are to do that in the Body of Christ. My friends called me and asked what I was doing. When I told them I was in the bed crying and depressed over the situation with my daughter, they reminded me of who I was.

"No, no, no, that is not who you are. No, come on. You need to get up. Come on, and you need to start laughing."

I told them, "I don't feel like laughing." But as tears fell down my face, I started laughing.

It felt like a sacrifice of praise because I didn't feel like it at all. Bill Johnson, the pastor at Bethel Church, where I was a member, talked often about the times you are the most broken, that is when you give the most exuberant, the most outrageous praise to God. So, as a parent, in the middle of the heartbreaking news of my child wanting to move away, I decided to laugh.

At first, it seemed superficial and fake, and with tears dripping down my face, I thought there was no point in this. At that moment I wasn't feeling better. But I kept doing it. Then suddenly, something happened, and I got my joy. The enemy wasn't going to steal my joy. Well, guess what? Six weeks later, my daughter came back. Praise God!

But the enemy kept trying. When I got over this hurdle my son now comes to me and says, "Mom, I want to go, I want to move, I want to go live with my dad."

He is younger, and he is the baby of the family.

I told God, "God, it was hard enough the first time, and I can't do this again! My heart is breaking, again."

But I let him go. I got a phone call on the way home after dropping him off at the airport.

"Hey, Kristina, can you lead treasure hunts tomorrow?" I said, "No, sorry, can't, absolutely not, there is no way. I feel so broken. I just put my son on a plane, and I am sad and broken."

She said, "I know. That is why I want you to lead treasure hunts tomorrow." Because she knew, she knew who I was, and she knew that I needed joy.

"You need to do this because it is your strength."

You have heard it, right? The joy of the Lord is my strength. So, I started laughing with tears dripping down my face; my son came home six months later. Come on, Jesus! God is good!

God is good, and I don't care what the circumstances are. I don't care if it is financial, and I don't care what it is. I have seen so many people healed and set free from bondages from laughter.

Laughing Daughter

I remember the time my daughter was in high school. She had some kids bullying her. I said to her, "When you go to school tomorrow, and they start calling you names, I want you to just turn to them, and I want you to laugh."

The next time it happened, she did it, and the craziest thing happened. They stopped! They didn't know what else to do. They stopped calling her names because the people attacking her suddenly had no place to land anymore. It had no place, because she just started laughing, and they couldn't respond because no words were coming out of her mouth. She wasn't saying anything - only laughter. She wasn't attacking them verbally or in any other way. She wasn't even going to start hurting them back verbally. She just started laughing, and they got frustrated and left. - Kristina

Gold Tooth

A friend of mine heard about my home group and wanted to join, but he didn't have time to come at night. He asked me if I would give him private lessons. I laughed and told him I would.

I spoke with him several times and gave him some homework to practice laughing. A few months later, he received a letter that his job had ended. He had a wife and children and did not know how he would tell them. He was the only income earner for his family. He started to sink into depression, but then he remembered what I had shared with him, and he began to laugh.

Now, this may sound like a crazy thing to do since he just lost his job. He has a family, house payments, and other bills. He had no idea what he would do, and he decides to laugh. He laughed for a while since he had several hours before he could make it back to his house. When he arrived, he started to speak to his wife, when suddenly, she saw something shiny in his mouth.

She said, "You have a gold tooth!"

He did not believe her, so he looked for himself. Sure enough, there was a gold tooth. He had not had any dental work done at all. He had just lost his job, and instead of worrying about what to do next, he started to laugh, and God gave him a gift. I had a chance to see the gold tooth with my own eyes, and it was gold. I knew what a gold tooth looked like since I had just paid a pretty penny for a gold crown, and he had received his as a gift from God.

People might say, "Why did God give him a gold tooth?"

Since he was not usually smiling, he would see what God had done for him every time he did.

I remember telling him, "Anytime he started to worry about what would happen, all he needed to do was open his mouth."

It turned out that after he lost his job, several weeks later, he ended up getting a better job that was much closer to his family. Praise Jesus!

A friend told me about an update on this story. The tooth fell out a few years later. He took it to be appraised, and they said, "It wasn't real gold." God colored his tooth just when he needed it, and then when it wasn't required, it came out, and the tooth was still the color gold. -Rich

Laughter

I was in a church service one time when laughter filled the congregation. I could feel it bubbling up inside of me like a little kid would belly laugh. I don't really know why we all laughed, but I could not stop. I left that church feeling like I had been changed from the inside out with amazing peace and refreshing. It was mind-blowing, which was exactly what I needed. - Sharon

Holy Laughter

This happened back in 1994. We had been to this renewal meeting. Toronto had just happened, and it was wild. I had never experienced any manifestation of the Spirit before. But some pastor friends prayed for me. Suddenly, this sensation started in my stomach and came out of my mouth as laughter out of nowhere. I laughed so hard I fell to the ground.

My mind was clear, and I was thinking, "What is happening to me? "

I felt embarrassed but could not stop. Back then, I was a pastor in AOG with a nice tie and suit. I don't know how long I laughed, but my stomach started hurting. I got up. I was late for dinner with some friends at their house. So, a friend and I took the car. He asked me what happened to me. I apologized and said, "I did not know." I just got hit with laughter while I was in God's presence.

First, the people in the house carried me into another room to calm down because I was laughing so hard. Then the people I drove with took me home and carried me to my bed. I live alone, and I still couldn't stop laughing. Then I finally fell asleep. I woke up and laughed some more and then slept again. I woke up and laughed hysterically in this sleeping pattern and then woke up laughing. This kept happening throughout the night.

The next day as I lay in my bed, I asked God what happened to me and why I couldn't stop laughing. Suddenly, I got this picture of this man in my head. In the past, every time I thought of him, pain would come. Even if I had forgiven him, the pain would not let go. But now, the pain was not there anymore. I was free! (This was not sexual abuse). - Sverre from Norway

My Prayer for You

I want to pray over you for whatever your situation is that you are going through. God can and will do great things for you no matter what you are facing.

> *"Holy Spirit, I thank You that You are the Comforter. I thank You that You are pure joy, Jesus. I release Your holy joy over every person reading this book. I release joy into our bodies, and I pray that the joy of the Lord would fill every person and that Your holy joy would be their strength. Let them feel like they can get through anything that comes their way. I pray that laughter would rise up in everyone's body. In Jesus' Name, Amen."*

Godly Lifestyle Activation

Whenever we go through a difficult circumstance, we can still try our best to find joy. We only need to remember that we will get through any hard times with God's help when things look the darkest. Those are the times when we have to remind ourselves that the best is still yet to come.

He will fill our mouths with laughter again. He will fill our mouths with shouts of joy. We will be able to look back at the most challenging times of our lives and say, "I know that I only got through those times with Your help Lord. I thank You for You are faithful and I praise You for helping me through them. Please help me focus on You, even more, when the next obstacle comes my way."

God's Truth

➢ Even when we don't think the Lord can or will do great things in our lives, He is already doing amazing things on our behalf behind the scenes. Eventually, we will see that He had a wonderful plan all along.

"The Lord has done great things for them." - Psalm 126:2 NKJV

➢ Even when we don't see the healing taking place with our own eyes or feel the healing within our minds, bodies, and souls, it doesn't mean that God isn't healing us one second, minute, and one day at a time. His healing requires us to trust Him fully with every aspect of our lives. Just because we don't see it or feel it doesn't mean that He isn't working on our behalf.

"Great crowds came to Him, bringing the lame, the blind, the crippled, the mute and many others, and laid them at his feet; and he healed them."
- Matthew 15:30 NIV

➢ God will bring us health in our bodies, minds, and souls in His timing and His ways. His ways are better than ours. We just have to trust Him.

"Nevertheless, I will bring health and healing to it; I will heal my people and will let them enjoy abundant peace and security" - Jeremiah 33:6 NIV

➢ We can shout for joy every day of our lives, despite our circumstances.

"Clap your hands, all you nations; shout to God with cries of joy."
- Psalm 47:1 NIV

➢ Whenever we ask for healing in Jesus' name, whether we feel it or see it, He is at work and is healing our lives, bodies, souls, and minds.

"Praise the Lord, my soul; all my inmost being, praise his holy name. Praise the Lord, my soul, and forget not all his benefits who forgives all your sins and heals all your diseases." - Psalm 103:1 NIV

"And Jesus went about all Galilee, teaching in their synagogues, preaching the gospel of the kingdom, and healing all kinds of sickness and all kinds of disease among the people. Then His fame went throughout all Syria, and they brought to Him all sick people who were afflicted with various diseases and torments, and those who were demon-possessed, epileptics, and paralytics; and He healed them." - Matthew 4:23-24 NKJV

➢ Whenever anxiety gets too much to handle, we can remember to try and be joyful despite our circumstances. There is no attack from the enemy that we can't counterattack with God's word.

"When anxiety was great within me, Your consolation brought me joy."
- Psalm 94:19 NIV

Your Response to God's Truth

Find people that you care about and laugh with them. If you want to build your relationships with your friends or family, then find time this week, call them up, spend time with them, and laugh together.

Laugh over people that you know need healing in their body.

Scriptures for Further Study

"But He was wounded for our transgressions, He was bruised for our iniquities; The chastisement for our peace was upon Him, And by His stripes, we are healed." - Isaiah 53:5 NKJV

"Why are you cast down, O my soul? And why are you disquieted within me? Hope in God, for I shall yet praise Him For the help of His countenance." - Psalm 42:5 NKJV

"You have turned for me my mourning into dancing; You have put off my sackcloth and clothed me with gladness," - Psalm 30:11 NKJV

"For you shall go out with joy and be led out with peace; The mountains and the hills Shall break forth into singing before you, and all the trees of the field shall clap their hands." - Isaiah 55:12 NKJV

"Now a leper came to Him, imploring Him, kneeling down to Him and saying to Him, "If You are willing, You can make me clean." Then Jesus, moved with compassion, stretched out His hand and touched him, and said to him, "I am willing; be cleansed." As soon as He had spoken, immediately the leprosy left him, and he was cleansed. And He strictly warned him and sent him away at once, and said to him, "See that you say nothing to anyone; but go your way, show yourself to the priest, and offer for your cleansing those things which Moses commanded, as a testimony to them." - Mark 1:40-44 NKJV

Chapter 10

Testimonies to Keep You Laughing

This chapter is about miracles to help you keep laughing and give you hope. These miracles will fill you with joy and help you see the amazing things that God has done and will keep doing.

I can attest that if you have ever been sick and then you get healed you will start laughing more over the goodness of God. If these seem too good to be true, all we need to do is look at all the amazing miracles God did that I am sure brought joy to the ones who received them in the Bible. So, as you read the following pages of incredible testimonies of the goodness of God, go ahead, start laughing and let the joy of the Lord be your strength so you too can receive your miracle.

Boy Healed of Cancer

I was ministering in Brazil one time and had the opportunity to pray for a precious little boy named Murillo. His mother, Sinara had brought him to be prayed over. He was very sick with a brain tumor; he could barely move and was also blind. At the time, I was not aware of all that was wrong with him, but I knew Jesus did, so we prayed. Our team prayed, spoke life over him, and laughed over the cancer. Two weeks after we prayed for him, we learned that they had taken him back to the doctor and the doctor said that the little boy was completely healed and would recover all his ability to move! His parents were so happy that they are going to do a conference for families in their city and they asked us to come back and speak. God is so good! -Kristina

Update: I recently received an update and learned that this little boy is now a healthy eleven-year-old young man and is doing very well! Praise the Lord!

Period Pain Healed

I used to have severe period pain, to the point of passing out multiple times. One night I was having such bad cramps I fell face down into the bathtub. Thankfully, I didn't hit my head or injure any part of my body, but I came to and felt around, thinking that I'd made it back to my bed. I remember feeling the cold tile of the bathtub and thinking, "wait, this isn't my bed."

I could barely open my eyes because of the severe pain and dizziness that I was experiencing. But after taking ibuprofen and using the heating pad, I was finally able to relax and get more sleep. During another one of my cycles, I was in such severe pain that I couldn't go to my college classes. In the middle of that horrible pain, I got a revelation from God. He asked me point-blank, "Did you pray about your severe pain? Have you ever asked Me to heal you? Pray about your pain! You don't have to live with this physical pain every month."

"OK, God, I'll start praying for my pain to go down to nothing."

I started praying and believing that my period pain would be way more manageable. He has graciously granted my prayer requests for the last few years. At times I barely notice that I'm on my period every month. To go from excruciating pain to being able to cope with it has been a true miracle in my life. I used to think that I would be in pain every month and dreaded my period coming on every single month. It isn't something that I look forward to, but now through God's mercy and grace, I can get through it with relative ease.

I even declare in my prayers that I know that God will continue to grant me healing from the severe pain. I'm so grateful that God has healed my body from how it used to be."- Alexis

Meeting Daughter

I believe that God has performed many miracles in my life! Big and small. The births of my daughters were both miracles. But I guess the biggest miracle at present in my life would be meeting my firstborn daughter, as an adult, after more than twenty-six and a half years! -Michelle

Miracle Baby

I was born three months too early and had a stroke when I was born. I had a grade-four brain bleed at twenty-eight weeks. My mom went into preterm labor, and the doctors put her on bed rest in the hospital. They kept giving her medication to try and stop the contractions, but the medicine didn't stop them. My dad was in another county when he got the call that my mom had gone into labor early. He sped on the highway and made it to the hospital in about twenty minutes. That drive should have taken him over an hour. They realized that I would be born whether they were ready for me or not. The doctors warned my parents of the complications that could ensue once I was born. These included brain bleeds, which are small strokes, jaundice, which is yellowing of the skin that has to be treated under high-pressure lights, and a feeding tube to help get nutrition in my body.

My dad even said, "As long as she isn't born on Friday the thirteenth." Sure enough, I was born on a Friday, the thirteenth. The doctors then told my parents that I wouldn't make it for more than a month. They even said if I did make it, my life would not be easy for them or me. They said I would be blind in one eye, deaf, mentally, and physically handicapped, and spend the rest of my life in a wheelchair. They also told my parents that I wouldn't go to regular schools, much less high school, or college. My parents didn't want to believe that news fully, so they prayed for a miracle over my life.

Then, the day before Thanksgiving, my parents got the call they dreaded. It was and is every parent's worst nightmare. They called my mom, saying, "You better come down to the hospital. Your daughter is dying. You need to start preparing for her funeral."

My parents and families rushed to the hospital to be with me and to say goodbye to me. They held a 24-hour prayer vigil over me, and my dad even made a deal with God as he begged Him to let me live and have a happy life.

He said, "Lord if you let my daughter live, I'll give my life over to you." God answered his prayer in more ways than one.

My vital signs started to improve, day by day. I was kept in the Neonatal Intensive Care Unit or the NICU for three months. With only weighing one pound nine ounces, my dad could hold me in the palm of his hand. His wedding ring fit around my entire arm because I was tiny.

Finally, on a freezing cold day on January 25th, they were able to bring me home. It was a challenge because we had a big snowstorm that day. Most babies don't have a problem with sucking their thumb. However, my arms were so weak that I couldn't even get my fist to my mouth. My mom and my therapist had to work hard with me to get my arms strengthened. To strengthen my legs, I had to have a tens unit, a bunch of sticky electrodes placed on the skin on my legs to get my reflexes to react.

My grandma, Anna, said my mom wouldn't take the news that I would be mentally and physically disabled for the rest of my life.

"Your mom only wanted what was best for you," said Anna. "She did everything she could to get you the best doctors, the best therapists, and when you turned two years old, she said to me, 'I can finally enjoy my child.'"

The therapy continued until I was thirteen years old. I would go to therapy multiple times a week to keep my mental and physical strength up. The therapy was grueling and exhausting, but it helped me in every way possible.

My dad always has a saying whenever he sees me getting discouraged and it's, "look at what you've already come through. There is nothing you can't do. You're an overcomer. I couldn't be prouder of you. Be proud of yourself. Be proud of the work you're doing."

The doctors are to this day, stunned at my miraculous recovery and escape from death. They are stunned by the fact that I can walk perfectly straight without the help of a walker, that I can see out of both eyes, and that I can talk normally and even function normally. I can drive a car. I sometimes look back on my life, and I am stunned at how far I've come. I went from a girl who had a stroke and wasn't even supposed to live to a girl who can walk perfectly straight, without a limp, and function completely normally.

It's all a miracle and the goodness of God. It's proof that God has a plan for my life, and I can't wait to see where God takes me. Knowing what I went through, looking back, and seeing how far I've come, only strengthens my resolve to work even harder to become a better person. I want to live my legacy with the gifts God has given me. - Alexis

Oil of Gladness

I was with an elderly woman – a prayer warrior for her whole life. She is now passed on. But the time I got to spend with her at the end of her life was a blessing to me. And in one of those meetings, she suddenly started raising her hands as if involuntarily and began laughing and laughing – and she was a bit embarrassed by it. But it was joyful, nonetheless. Immediately I understood it was the oil of gladness. It was such a sweet moment. -Joern from Norway

More Testimonies:
Gas Miracle

One day I asked God what His strategy was for a situation, and He reminded me of a song that had the lyrics of "a thankful heart prepares the way for you, my God." I had no gas money to get me and my family from point A to point B. So, I prayed and was handed $22.00 from a complete stranger. I was then able to pay $20.00 for gas for myself and I was also able to give two dollars as a gift back to God as a tithe. I was even able to bless someone else with gas as I gave half of the $20.00 to someone else who needed gas.

I went to put the ten dollars of gas in my vehicle when another Christian came and filled my tank with gas. Because of that kind person I was able to bless someone else and paid for their gas with the ten dollars I had left in my hand." -Kristina

Turkey Dinner

There was a time in my life when I needed groceries as the cupboards were getting bare in my house and I knew I needed food desperately for me and my children. I brought my situation to God, and I prayed over my cupboards. Then, ten minutes later my phone rang and the person on the other end was asking if I wanted a turkey dinner. At first, I said, "No, I am sure someone else can use it," since I had plans for Thanksgiving.

Then the lady said again, "Would you like turkey dinner?

I finally said, "Yes."

A few hours later, food boxes arrived with much more than just a turkey dinner. I had more than enough." After that, we went to church and a lady there handed us more groceries in a bag. When we got home, we pulled out all of our favorite sweets, not just popcorn, but kettle corn, my kids' favorite pop tarts, and cookies. When my kids saw all this, they exclaimed, "Jesus loves junk food!" Ha ha ha! This lady did not know us, but the Lord had given her a mission to go to the store and purchase these items for us. God cares about the smallest details of our lives including these special treats. -Kristina

Bank Parking Lot Miracle

One day, I went to the bank and could not help but overhear a lady sharing how her husband had passed away, and her baby had died. Little did I know what would happen next, but God knew exactly what was about to happen.

I walked outside and saw her heading to her car. I called out to her, saying, "Hi. I couldn't help but overhear what happened to your family. Can I pray for you?"

She said I could. I prayed for God to remove the tape playing in her head about her family dying and that God would heal her heart. She shared how she had remarried and had a son that was thirty years old at the time.

She had been replaying the incident of her former husband and baby dying like it was yesterday for over thirty years. Well, if that were all, that would have been amazing. But God was not done with her story.

I said goodbye, and she walked away, and then I felt I was supposed to ask her about her back. At first, I blew it off. But since it persisted, I took a chance and daringly shouted out, "Do you have something going on with your back? Are you in pain?"

She stopped and said, "How do you know I broke my back?"

I explained how I felt the Lord was showing me He wanted to heal her back. I also shared a couple of short testimonies and prayed over her, and instantly there was heat on her back. After releasing the peace of heaven over her, I could tell God was breaking the trauma off her. Then, I had her test it out.

She said, "It feels better."

So, I said, "Try and do something you usually can't do."

That is when she started twisting, and her eyes got big. Then she shared how she had had many surgeries and was supposed to get surgery again. She had been dealing with the pain for years. It was a pain level six before we prayed over her pain together.

Praise Jesus that her heart and back were healed, which is enough to shout out with joy and praise Him for. But God had one more thing He wanted to do for her.

I then asked her if she knew Jesus. I also asked her if she knew that I wasn't the one who healed her from her back pain. Jesus was. She shared how she had asked Jesus to heal her a long time ago but walked away from Him and tried to do it all on her own. I asked her if she would like to let Jesus be the Lord of her life.

In the Chase Bank parking lot, she said yes, gave her heart to Jesus, and forgave all her enemies. That was a big deal since she was a Native American who had her identity stripped away from her by her people. But Jesus gave her a new identity in Him that day. Jesus healed her heart, body, and soul all at the bank. Here is to living naturally, supernaturally.

When we say "yes", He comes, and we see Him do great things loving the ones in front of us. All it takes is a yes, and He does the rest. -Kristina

Food Miracle

Another time, I had no groceries for my children and me. Again, I prayed about my situation and came home. As I walked through the house, I found my kitchen table covered with bags of groceries and my freezer and fridge filled too. Prayer does wonders. -Kristina

Miracle Heat

Another time, I had no heat in my house as the oil to keep the heat going ran out. This was during Christmas, so no one was working during the holidays. I prayed about our desperate situation. God supplied enough paper and boxes from presents to keep the fire burning in the house for a couple of days until more oil could be brought to our home. -Kristina

Car Miracle

God answered another of my prayers when He knew I needed a car. I prayed and believed that somehow God would provide for me. Finally, God provided a car and title so I could drive the car. -Kristina

Clothes Miracle

Another time God answered my prayers for help was when I needed clothes for my daughter. I knew God already knew what kind of clothes my daughter liked. Through prayer and the generosity of people, I received brand-name clothes that looked brand new. Some of the clothes still had tags on them. -Kristina

Miracle Mission Trip

One year, I was supposed to go on a mission trip. I knew I needed money to go on this mission trip. So, I prayed for the funds to show up, and God granted the answers to my requests. God provided for us so much that not just one trip was paid for, but four or five trips were paid in full. Two mission trips were to Mexico. Two trips were to South Africa, and one trip was to Indiana. -Kristina

New Tires

One winter, I needed new tires for my car, so I prayed for God to give me a way to get new snow tires for the car. God came through again and provided me with brand new snow tires. - Kristina

Miracle Hotel Room

Another time God provided for my family and me was when I needed a hotel room for my children and me to sleep in for the night. But unfortunately, I was short on cash to pay for the room we needed. A stranger walked into the hotel at midnight and covered the hotel expenses for my children and me. -Kristina

Weight Loss Miracle

Here is another amazing testimony. There was a lady who had liver problems and diabetes. She came for healing, and we were able to help her over Skype. She was overweight and wanted to be healed from her liver problems and diabetes problems. We laughed over her. The next day, she felt like her jeans were a little loose. So, she weighed herself and found out that she had lost fifteen pounds overnight, which was ten percent of her body weight. She was just doing some due diligence, and she said her weight had been around 174 pounds for some time. So, it seemed impossible that she lost all that weight in only one day. One of the sisters saw her that day after school and said she looked like she had lost weight. According to her doctors, for her to lose ten percent of her body weight would help take away her diabetes and prevent any more liver problems from persisting. Jesus knows exactly how to heal. — Woman from China

Provision Vision

Here is another amazing testimony from a lady that received a remarkable breakthrough in her life through laughter.

"So, after laughing, I went to sleep. I slept better than I ever remember. Since I moved here, I have woken up several times during the night with excruciating migraines, and I usually have my teeth clenched from stress all night. Most mornings, I have a cloud of gloom hanging over me, reminding me of everything I have to do, all I don't have, and everything I need.

I'm reminded that I don't have what it takes to meet our needs. But then, one night, I had incredible dreams that were so inclined with what God was saying in the path of my destiny. Certain people were in the dream, and it was incredible.

I woke up at 6:00 a.m. and spent the entire morning worshiping God and having deep intimacy with God. I was finally forced out of my room by my kids at 11:00 a.m. I was having deep visions and incredible words spoken over me through Him and by Him alone. It was a huge breakthrough, and there are so many more to come for me. I am still laughing at the minuscule bumps that we call problems that are posted on Facebook. Through God's help, there are no problems." -Kate

Covid 19 Testimony

While finishing up the editing of my book this last month my husband and I both came down with the infamous Covid 19. We were sick with body aches, massive headaches that felt like our head was in a vice for days, sore throats, and fevers. Mine was running about 102.9 for several days. During this horrible sickness, we found a way to laugh. Yes, you heard me right. We were practicing laughing. I can promise you nothing inside us wanted to laugh but we know the power of laughter. So, to help us get our ha ha started, we watched episode after episode for hours of the old Dick Van Dyke Show. You might think ok what is so profound about the Dick Van Dyke Show? Well, guess who was in Mary Poppins? Yes, you guessed it, Dick Van Dyke. God used a simple black-and-white show to help us laugh so we could increase our immune system and fight this awful sickness that was attacking our bodies with a vengeance. Of course, we also prayed and had many others praying for us too. The good news is this time God didn't have to tell me it was time to laugh. See, when you have been cultivating it in your life for years it starts to spill out a whole lot easier. We still went through the sickness with tears and pain, but it didn't take us down and we continued to laugh to build our body, soul, and our spirit in the middle of the storm. Remember "it's just a laughing matter" ha, ha, ha, ha. -Kristina

The Oil of Joy

I want to leave you with one last testimony. It is simply amazing!

We've already read about the oil of joy in a previous testimony but let me share one more. Remember, I used to have a home group called Laugh Out Loud and all we did was laugh over situations. There was a lady who had a very severe case of eczema that came to this home group. The eczema was all over her hands. She had it so bad that she had scars where her hands had been totally riddled with bumps and all kinds of problems, but it wasn't just on her hands, it was on her arms, legs, and all over her body.

Now you know women; we like to look beautiful, and we put makeup on to cover up little blemishes and divots. She would try to cover those scars left from the years of dealing with eczema. One day we just started laughing over her and suddenly the most amazing thing happened; oil literally started to drip from her fingers! As soon as we saw it, I grabbed her hand and I put the oil against my hand because I had never seen this before. I had heard about it, but I had never seen it. Then we started putting it on each other. It just kept coming!

The next morning, she called me. "Kristina, this oil is still coming out of my fingers!" I said, "You know what? Why don't you start putting it on your body? Why don't you start using it like a lotion?"

She did exactly that and in a matter of weeks, all of her scaring was gone! Her skin was like baby skin. It was the oil of joy for the spirit of heaviness - the heaviness of not feeling beautiful, that heaviness of feeling sick all the time. Everything had changed!

So, I just release that over you. I release more grace for you to walk in the fullness of joy and the fullness of who you are called to be. Remember that laughter *is* God's medicine for healing your body, your soul, and your spirit. Be blessed! -Kristina

Godly Lifestyle Activation

Our testimony is not just for us but it's also to give hope to others that they can receive a miracle and breakthrough in their life too. That's why the second part of Revelation 19:10 says the testimony of Jesus is the spirit of prophecy. That means that God wants to do it again and He uses our testimony to give people faith and hope for their very own testimony because if God did it for us then He will do it for someone else too. All we have to do is ask.

God's Truth

> **If Jesus can heal this man, we can have faith that He will heal us.**

"There he found a certain man named Aeneas, who had been bedridden eight years and was paralyzed. And Peter said to him, "Aeneas, Jesus the Christ heals you. Arise and make your bed." Then he arose immediately."
- Acts 9:33-34 NKJV

> God gave the disciples the power to heal the sick, cure diseases, and release the enemy's strongholds on many people in the Bible. He is still at work today doing the same things for us and in us, not to mention through us today.

"...that word you know, which was proclaimed throughout all Judea, and began from Galilee after the baptism which John preached: 38 how God anointed Jesus of Nazareth with the Holy Spirit and with power, who went

about doing good and healing all who were oppressed by the devil, for God was with Him." - Acts 10:37-38 NKJV

➤ When you work hard for the Lord, He will reward us.

"When you eat the labor of your hands, you shall be happy, and it shall be well with you." - Psalm 128:2 NKJV

➤ The Lord will give us a crown of beauty instead of ashes when we are united with Him in heaven one day. Even though times can be challenging, we must try to rest in Him and on His eternal promises of bringing us to Him in heaven one day. When times get tough, we can laugh and say, "look at what I have to look forward to because of Jesus and His ultimate sacrifice. He loved me enough that He was willing to take my place on the cross and take my punishment as His own, even though He did nothing to deserve it. I can laugh and enjoy my life to the fullest because that is what God wants me to do.

"To console those who mourn in Zion, to give them beauty for ashes, The oil of joy for mourning, The garment of praise for the spirit of heaviness; That they may be called trees of righteousness, The planting of the Lord, that He may be glorified." - Isaiah 61:3 NKJV

Your Response to God's Truth

Make a recording of you laughing today, or you can ask others to help you make one. This is another amazing way to remember to laugh on the days when it's not easy to laugh.

Today listen to laughing hyenas on the internet and listen to laughing babies and see how your mood changes.

Scriptures for Further Study

"Blessed are you who hunger now, for you shall be filled Blessed are you who weep now, for you shall laugh." - Luke 6:21 NKJV

"These things I have spoken to you, that My joy may remain in you, and that your joy may be full." - John 15:11 NKJV

"And Sarah said, "God has made me laugh, and all who hear will laugh with me." - Genesis 21:6 NKJV

"He will yet fill your mouth with laughing, And your lips with rejoicing." - Job 8:21 NKJV

"Why are you cast down, O my soul? And why are you disquieted within me? Hope in God, for I shall yet praise Him For the help of His countenance." - Psalm 42:5 NKJV

Chapter 11

Pass the Baton

"Then the Lord answered me and said, "Write the vision and make it plain on tablets, that he may run who reads it." - Habakkuk 2:2 NKJV

Now it's time to write your testimony. Write your own words here in this chapter. Write what God has done for you. What miracles has He given to you? Let the written testimony of your words be here to look at and remind yourself of the goodness and power of God in your life.

Make it plain and make it simple for others to read it. Show them this page as you run into people that need to hear of the testimony of your life and miracles.

This page was left blank on purpose for you to add your story. Please do so at any time and let God be praised! Don't forget to laugh! Ha ha ha!

_____

_____

_____

_____

_____

_____

_____

_____

_____

_____

Conclusion

I have seen so many people healed and set free through the unique gift of laughter God has given every one of us. God recently provided another download to me on this fantastic subject. When I thought that I learned everything I could about laughter. After years of sharing joy and laughter in many different places worldwide, God gave me a deeper understanding of the meaning of Joy from His word. It comes from Psalm 16:11, which says, "You make known to me the path of life; You will fill me with joy in your presence, with eternal pleasures at your right hand."

He said, "Kristina, you know anybody can laugh. But the only way you can experience the greatest joy that can only be found in My presence is by being in My company. When you're in the presence of the Lord, that's the only time you can receive the fullness of joy."

As we spend time in His presence, that's where we get that fullness of joy. It comes as we spend time with God. He will fill us with unspeakable joy that is not just head knowledge but also heart knowledge. He wants us to be set free and live a life with so much fun, love, and laughter that it is contagious. He wants us to live with such joy that it will cause others to desire to know how to have the same joy that we carry.

Be blessed.

Prayer

Dear Jesus, I pray for everyone reading this book that their lives would be touched and impacted by You and through Your never-ending grace and love. I pray that everyone feels Your love surrounding them every day of their lives. I pray that everyone that reads this book experiences joy and laughter that can only come through knowing You as their Lord and Savior.

Thank You for the ability to know You and call on You every day of our lives. Help everyone understand what it is like to experience the true joy of having You in their lives. Thank You for the joy You bring to us every day. Help all of us want to know You more and experience the joy of laughter.

I pray for every person reading this book right now that their lives would never be the same and radically filled with so much joy. I pray that it would be so contagious that people around them would notice and say the same thing my children said to me, "what happened to you? Why are you so happy?"

I pray that everyone will find joy. If anyone reading this is dealing with depression. If they are dealing with anxiety or any sickness, that laughter would be their portion to help assist them in their healing.

I pray that if they are coping with any suicidal thoughts or hopelessness, they will find hope through laughter. I pray the same joy that overtook me in South Africa will also touch them. I pray that people would see the supernatural joy which took me over 40-plus years to find and that they would receive it at an accelerated pace.

I release the ha ha anointing. I pray that God would take all your pain and turn it into joy.

Thank You, Lord, for every person who has taken the time to read this book. I pray the revelation they receive in this book will be only a starting point for them to experience more joy than they have ever known.

I pray that marriages, families, and other relationships will be restored as they take the keys they have received from reading this book. I pray that they will have more laughter that will bring healing to their bodies, souls, and spirits and that they will be able to receive it for themselves and give it away to others.

Finally, I pray that any voids that people are dealing with will be filled in their search for You, Lord. Remind them gently, Lord, that they will find joy and peace in only one place, a relationship with Jesus.

I pray if anyone reading this doesn't know Him personally, that He will give them the desire to know Him more every day. Just like His word says, it is the goodness of God that leads man to repentance. I pray that everyone reading this would feel the tangible feeling of being happy, maybe for the first time in their lives, like so many I have had a chance to minister to around the world. I pray that their sadness will be replaced with laughter and love. In Jesus' name. Amen.

About The Author

Kristina Khan is married and resides in California. She has two grown children. She has had a pastoral license as a minister and graduated from Simpson University with a Bachelor of Arts degree in Organizational Leadership, she is also a graduate of Bethel School of Supernatural Ministry. She co-led treasure hunts in the School of Ministry for 5 years. She has led teams all over the world releasing God's goodness both in the church and community. Kristina's areas of ministry have included leading outreach, overseeing Firestarters discipleship program at Bethel for over 3 years, leading a home group, coaching students and church attendees, and traveling to churches to speak on healing, evangelism, the prophetic, identity, leadership, and laughter. She has traveled internationally and seen many miracles, signs, and wonders. Kristina has a heart to release others into their destiny by experiencing God's love through joy and encounters with God. She has a heart to see revival released everywhere she goes.

References

1. https://bit.ly/3ciKazH
2. http://www.laughingmatters.org/why-laughter.html
3. https://elijahlist.com/words/display_word/7670
4. Happily Ever Laughter | Psychology Today
5. Happily Ever Laughter | Psychology Today
6. Paras Hospitals
7. Laughter - metrohealth (metrohealthdc.org)
8. Study Shows Laughter Reducing Heart Disease Risk - Good News Network
9. https://www.mayoclinic.org/healthy-lifestyle/stress-management/in-depth/stress-relief/art-20044456
10. Laughter is the Best Medicine - HelpGuide.org
11. How Does Laughter Can Relieve Stress | USAHS
12. https://www.gaiam.com/blogs/discover/7-health-benefits-of-laughter
13. How do B cells and T cells work to fight disease? - POZ
14. Scientific benefits of laughter for physical, mental and social health- FactDr
15. Stress relief from laughter? It's no joke - Mayo Clinic
16. https://iheartintelligence.com/laughter-increases-memory-abilities/
17. The power of laughter for cancer patients | CTCA (cancercenter.com)
18. https://www.gilmorehealth.com/laughter-may-be-the-cure-to-depression-anxiety-and-much-more/
19. Laughter Therapy - An Effective Treatment - nmmra.org
20. Why Laughter Is Good For Mental Health (laughteronlineuniversity.com)
21. https://feedreader.com/observe/lifehack.org/articles%2Flifestyle%2F9-surprising-benefits-laughter-you-need-know.html%3F+itemId=707388395
22. Laughing Burns Calories! – Passion (psu.edu)
23. Laughter is the Best Medicine - HelpGuide.org
24. 9 Benefits of Laughter and What You Need To Know (amindbend.com)
25. Stress relief from laughter? It's no joke - Mayo ClinicStress relief from laughter? It's no joke - Mayo Clinic
26. The Power of Humor in Ideation and Creativity | Psychology Today
27. Positive Emotions and Your Health | NIH News in Health
28. bul-1316803.pdf (apa.org)
29. Seven ways laughter can improve your well-being | Wu Tsai Neurosciences Institute (stanford.edu)
30. https://www.psychologytoday.com/us/blog/let-their-words-do-the-talking/201608/people-will-you-if-you-make-them-laugh
31. https://www.cnbc.com/2021/07/08/why-laughter-can-make-you-more-productive-at-work.html
32. Managing Conflict with Humor - HelpGuide.org

33. Managing Conflict with Humor - HelpGuide.org
34. Why laughter can make you more productive at work (cnbc.com)
35. 8 Amazing Facts About Humor in the Workplace - Article (intuit.com)
36. Humor Can Increase Hope, Research Shows -- ScienceDaily
37. How Laughter Brings Us Together (berkeley.edu)
38. https://www.sciencedaily.com/releases/2005/02/050211095658.htm
39. Can laughter cure illness? | HowStuffWorks
40. http://www.patchadams.org
41. Military Suicide Rates Are at an All-Time High; Here's How We're Trying to Help · United Service Organizations (uso.org)
42. Suicide Statistics and Facts – SAVE
43. The Healing Benefits of Humor and Laughter - Whole Health Library (va.gov)
44. The Healing Benefits of Humor and Laughter - Whole Health Library (va.gov)
45. Mary Poppins (1964) - IMDb
46. Bias Strips (uky.edu)
47. Shared Laughter In a Relationship Indicates a Happier Couple | Time
48. How Laughter Brings Us Together (berkeley.edu)
49. Putting Laughter in Context: Shared Laughter as Behavioral Indicator of Relationship Well-Being - PMC (nih.gov)
50. Happily Ever Laughter | Psychology Today
51. Happily Ever Laughter | Psychology Today
52. Happily Ever Laughter | Psychology Today
53. Effect of Workplace Laughter Groups on Personal Efficacy Beliefs | Heidi Beckman; Nathan Regier; Judy Young | download (booksc.me)
54. Effect of Workplace Laughter Groups on Personal Efficacy Beliefs | Heidi Beckman; Nathan Regier; Judy Young | download (booksc.me)
55. Effect of Workplace Laughter Groups on Personal Efficacy Beliefs | Heidi Beckman; Nathan Regier; Judy Young | download (booksc.me)
56. Effect of Workplace Laughter Groups on Personal Efficacy Beliefs | Heidi Beckman; Nathan Regier; Judy Young | download (booksc.me)

Made in the USA
Middletown, DE
28 October 2022

13685960R00096